HISTORY & SCIENCE

All the Facts
That Turned Out to Be Myths

Emma Marriott & Graeme Donald

Reader's
digest

The Reader's Digest Association, Inc.
New York, NY • Montreal

A READER'S DIGEST BOOK

First published in Great Britain in 2011 by Michael O'Mara Books Limited, 9 Lion Yard, Tremadoc Road, London SW4 7NQ.

ISBN 978-1-62145-286-7

They Got It Wrong: History & Science comprises two books previously published by Reader's Digest:

> *They Got It Wrong: History*
> Copyright © 2013 Michael O'Mara Books Limited
> ISBN 978-1-62145-008-5
> Credits: Maps and technical drawings by David Woodroofe. Illustrations by Andrew Pinder.

> *They Got It Wrong: Science*
> Copyright © 2013 Michael O'Mara Books Limited
> ISBN 978-1-62145-009-2
> Credits: Pages 31 and 35: www.karenswhimsy.com/public-domain-images. Page 55: Mary Evans Picture Library/Interfoto Agentur. Page 57: © Science Museum/Science & Society Picture Library (all rights reserved). Page 65: Library of Congress (LC-DIG-ppm-sca-27955). Page 71: © The Art Archive/Alamy. Pages 84 and 124: www.clipart.com. Page 87: Walter Daran/Time & Life Pictures/Getty Images. Page 112: Courtesy of Institute for Nearly Genius Research, www.bonkersinstitute.org. Page118: Interfoto/ Sammlung Rauch/ Mary Evans Picture Library. Page 122: Miles Kelly/fotoLibra.

We are committed to both the quality of our products and the service we provide to our customers. We value your comments, so please feel free to contact us.
> The Reader's Digest Association, Inc.
> Adult Trade Publishing
> 44 South Broadway
> White Plains, NY 10601

For more Reader's Digest products and information, visit our website:
> www.rd.com (in the United States)
> www.readersdigest.ca (in Canada)

Printed in the United States of America

1 3 5 7 9 10 8 6 4 2

CONTENTS

History

Science

THEY GOT IT WRONG

History

All the **Facts** That Turned Out to Be **Myths**

Emma Marriott

Reader's
digest

The Reader's Digest Association, Inc.

New York, NY / Montreal

CONTENTS

‹∽○∾›

The main killing sites of the Holocaust
were Auschwitz and the
concentration camps in Germany.

Benito Mussolini made the trains run on time.

The defeat of the Spanish Armada was a heroic
victory for the English and the beginning of
their supremacy of the seas.

Captain Scott: Intrepid Antarctic explorer
and iconic British hero.

French Revolutionary doctor Joseph Guillotin
invented the guillotine.

The Man in the Iron Mask was Louis XIV's brother.

Australia was established purely as a penal colony, a
dumping ground for Britain's convicts.

President Roosevelt's New Deal saved capitalism and
lifted the United States out of the Depression.

Abraham Lincoln's main aim in fighting the
Civil War was to free the slaves.
96

The United States entered World War I at the last minute
and contributed little to the Allied victory.
104

The Great Famine in China was the unintentional
consequence of Chairman Mao's economic reforms.
112

James Watt invented the steam engine.
119

The attack on Pearl Harbor was deliberately
engineered by President Roosevelt.
124

The Italian astronomer Galileo was persecuted by the
Catholic Church and imprisoned in a dark cell.
130

Bloody Mary was a ruthless persecutor of
English Protestants.
136

St. Patrick was Irish.
142

Roman gladiators fought to the death.
147

INTRODUCTION

"History is a pack of lies about events that never happened told by people who weren't there."
—George Santayana

The chronicles of history are littered with myths and legends, misinformation, falsehoods, embellishment, wild exaggeration, and a whole lot of confusion. All this makes for an awful lot of "bad" history. As Mr. Santayana says, the problem with history is that we weren't actually there, and we rely on other people who also weren't there to tell us what happened and why. This means that historical "facts"—like the ones drilled into us at school—are not quite what they seem. The best we can say for a lot of them is that they are "probably true," while others—like that Lincoln's main goal of the Civil War was the emancipation of the slaves or that St. Patrick was Irish—turn out to be, well, probably not true.

There are a myriad of reasons why events or people

from the past are misrepresented or misunderstood. Archaeological or documentary evidence may be lacking, unreliable, or bewilderingly inconsistent (ask ten or twenty witnesses what happened at a particular incident, and you'll get ten or twenty different versions). Extrapolating what happened at any given event is a tricky business. If you then add in a large chunk of time, be it a decade or several centuries, some might say it's an almost impossible task.

Problems also arise when we wrench something out of the past and examine it out of context. We can't pretend we don't live in the present, and no matter how much we try, modern sensibilities shape our view of history—and the conclusions that we draw often speak volumes about our own beliefs. In the last century, Captain Scott was revered as a great explorer; now many think of him as an ill-advised fool. Which is it to be? And which is the example of "bad" history?

History, like life, is annoyingly complex (and confusing); so packaging the past into a neat story so that it fits some kind of preconceived notion has its dangers. We liken our historical figures to imaginary characters, and assign to them the familiar stereotypes of either hero or villain. We forget, however, that they were real-life people, who, like us, were probably a combination of good and bad. We much prefer our victories in battle to be resounding and decisive, and not, like many military engagements, muddled, open-ended, and inconsequential. While these embellishments make for exciting stories—we all love a dashing hero or a resounding victory—they also distort the truth, endorse delusions of grandeur, and perpetuate many of the myths with which we are so familiar.

Historical myths, like fairy tales, are generally quite harmless, but when they are seized upon as political weaponry, the consequences can be disastrous. Repressive regimes can cover up a discreditable past or rewrite the history books with their own sanitized version of events (see Chairman Mao on page 112), and propagandists and political leaders can appropriate popular historical myths to lend authority to their own rather dubious belief systems (see Otto von Bismarck on page 25). Conversely, some theorists who are hellbent on proving some kind of government conspiracy or cover-up can also wander into rather sketchy territory (see the attack on Pearl Harbor on page 124).

What follows is an investigation into some of the myths and falsehoods that have become entrenched in popular belief and wrongly influenced our understanding of the world. It is by no means exhaustive—there are without a doubt many more myths out there—but I hope it goes some way to shedding light on some of the worst offenses. Some will disagree with the findings—I too "wasn't there," and, as the historian Pieter Geyl said (at least, I hope he said it), "History is an argument without end." But I'm hoping that the history passed down to us is not *all* a pack of lies, that lurking within what they got wrong are some truths—we just need to keep looking for them.

—Emma Marriott

The Old West was a wild and dangerous place to be.

Few areas of history have gripped the imagination as much as the expansion of the United States into the wilderness of the West. Sensational tales of the "Wild West" portrayed a violent and brutal land where hardy settlers rubbed alongside brave cowboys, ruthless outlaws, and savage Indians, where people took the law into their own hands to protect their families.

This image of the Old West proved hugely popular and was consolidated in folklore, music, and dime novels that sold millions of copies in the second half of the nineteenth century. Soldier and showman Buffalo Bill Cody similarly popularized the legend of the frontier through his Wild West shows. In 1893, Buffalo Bill's show featured a new act of "Rough Riders" consisting of marksmen from all over the world—including future President Theodore Roosevelt.

In the twentieth century, the legend of the Wild West spread to the rest of the world as artists, magazines, and movies spun a whole industry around its mythologization, in which gun-slinging heroes battled against "Injuns" in places where, as Sergio Leone put it, "life has no value." The first Western movie, *The Great Train Robbery*, came out in 1903, and by the 1950s, the genre was also lapped up by television audiences, who could choose from no fewer than twenty-six prime-time Western series in 1959.

Yet the reality of life in the West was quite different from the general lawlessness depicted in the movies. Recent research has shown that crime was relatively low among the West's settlers and that you were more likely to be gunned down in Victorian London than in the Wild West. In the real Dodge City, which at one point was thought of as the biggest and rowdiest town of the Wild West, a total of five deaths in 1878 amounted to the town's worst year for homicides.

Similarly, the legendary shoot-out at the O.K. Corral—a gunfight between two gangs led by Wyatt Earp and Ike Clanton (and regarded as the most famous gun battle in the history of the Old West)—lasted all of sixty seconds and resulted in just three deaths. Face-offs at "high noon" were not common events, and gunfights were usually spontaneous and the result of drunken arguments that had got out of hand. The Wild West mythmakers would also have us believe that bank robberies were everyday events, but Larry Schweikart of the University of Dayton has estimated that between 1859 and 1900 just *twelve* bank robberies occurred along the Western frontier.

Research has also shown that, in the absence of any formal government, settlers devised surprisingly effective ways to protect themselves from all manner of crimes. Voluntary organizations in the form of "wagon-train" governments were set up to police and protect the 300,000 pioneers traveling west to California and Oregon. In the Midwest, land clubs and cattlemen associations settled disputes and enforced property rights. On the West Coast, gold-mining districts set up legal systems that punished crimes against life and property. On the whole, miners avoided violence and abided by the rules of the district. Andrew Morriss of the University of Alabama School of Law writes, "This amazing polyglot of men seeking rapid wealth, and with virtually no intention of building a lasting society, created a set of customary legal institutions which not only flourished in California but successfully adapted to conditions across the West."

MINI MYTH

COWBOYS

Also central to the Wild West myth was the gun-slinging cowboy, the embodiment of the brave lone rider, who, we're led to believe, overran the frontier. In reality, farmers outnumbered cowboys in the West by about a *thousand* to one: there were (at the most) only 10,000 working cowboys, the majority of whom were Hispanic, African-American, or Mexican. Few cowboys could afford a firearm (a modern Colt weapon represented an average nine months' salary), and many died young—not from shoot-outs but from riding accidents or illnesses borne from a hard but decidedly unglamorous life herding cows across vast plains.

Other old West myths, largely popularized by the entertainment industry, include the image of westward migrants lumbering across the Great Plains in Conestoga wagons (large wagons pulled by oxen). In fact, most families used much smaller covered wagons called "prairie schooners," which were hauled by mules or oxen. In addition, wagon trails were not constantly assailed by Native Americans—most pioneers crossed the plains without incident; nor would trails of wagons defend themselves from attacking Indians by maneuvering themselves into galloping circles (the movies borrowed this from the Wild West shows in which limited arena space necessitated the circular formation). Any killings by Native Americans tended to be wildly exaggerated: of the half a million people who passed through Western territories in wagon trains between 1840 and 1860, it's estimated that just 362 died from attacks by hostile natives.

And yet, while bloodshed was relatively low among the West's new settlers, life for America's indigenous population was increasingly brutal. As migrants advanced west, Native Americans were uprooted and moved from their homelands, and many died as a result of war, disease, or loss of livelihood. Between 1830 and 1895 the number of Native Americans fell from 2 million to 90,000, while around 70 million buffalo (the Plains Indians' main source of livelihood) were slaughtered.

The myth of the Wild West has captivated millions across the world and spawned a huge publishing and entertainment industry in the process. In the forging of the new nation of America, exaggerated tales of brave and hardy white men venturing into the unknown have proved far more appealing than the reality of the migrants' grittier, more mundane lives or the brutalities inflicted upon the West's indigenous population. This mythical depiction of the Wild West, perpetuated by Hollywood, was brilliantly satirized by Mel Brooks's 1974 film *Blazing Saddles*, none more so than in Sheriff Bart's farewell to the townspeople of Rock Ridge:

> *Bart:* Work here is done. I'm needed elsewhere now. I'm needed wherever outlaws rule the West, wherever innocent women and children are afraid to walk the streets, wherever a man cannot live in simple dignity, wherever a people cry out for justice.
>
> *Crowd:* [in unison] BULLSHIT!
>
> *Bart:* All right, you caught me. Speaking the plain truth is getting pretty damn dull around here.

REALITY CHECK
NATIVE AMERICAN CUSTOMS

Western movies and popular novels got it wrong: Native Americans did not greet each other with "how." Similarly, "Paleface" and "Great White Father" were the invention of novelists like James Fenimore Cooper (*The Last of the Mohicans*). Indians did not send coded messages to other tribes via smoke signals, nor was scalping a common practice (though it was actually introduced by the white settler). The Native American showed as little concern for their environment as their white counterpart, reducing the population of beavers and the white-tailed deer to near extinction. The image of the Native Americans as the original environmentalist largely stems from a much-quoted 1854 speech by Suquamish Chief Seattle: ". . . the earth does not belong to man—man belongs to the earth. . . ." However, it's possible that these words bear no relation to those actually spoken by Chief Seattle, as he delivered the speech in the language of Lushootseed, which was simultaneously translated into Chinook Jargon. A Dr. Henry Smith reproduced the speech from memory in 1887, and various adaptations have appeared ever since.

The Founding Fathers sought to replace monarchy with democracy.

The U.S. Constitution, written in 1787 in Philadelphia, established the foundation of the government as we know it today—the two legislative houses of Congress (the House of Representatives and Senate), the executive branch of the presidency, and the judicial arm of the Supreme Court. As the Constitution provided the framework for representative democracy in the United States, it seems only reasonable to presume that the Founding Fathers—the men who wrote the Constitution—intended to establish a nation based upon democratic principles.

In reality, the Founding Fathers—which included such luminaries as Benjamin Franklin and George Washington—were wholly united in their opposition to and mistrust of democracy. For them, and for many of their contemporaries, democracy equaled mob rule and anarchy, and the word itself had somewhat dubious associations. The fifty-five delegates who devised and worded the Constitution were largely members of the gentry and lawyers, and a third of them had served in Washington's army. While showing a great deal of intellect and foresight, they shared a conservative outlook and were not shy in voicing their hostility towards democracy. Delegate Edmund Randolph spoke of the "follies and turbulence of democracy," while Roger Sherman said that "the people immediately should have as little to do as may be about the Government."

MINI MYTH

INSIDE GEORGE WASHINGTON'S HEAD

One of the most prevalent myths about George Washington is that he was outfitted with wooden teeth. It is true that he was plagued by bad teeth through his life, as well as many other health ailments. By the time he was inaugurated he only had one original tooth left in his head, but his dentures were far fancier than some whittled, wooden choppers. The day he became the first president, he wore dentures made from elephant and hippopotamus ivory, human teeth, and gold. This set of false teeth was spring-loaded to keep them in place. Perhaps this explains why he never smiled in a portrait.

Although the delegates favored a government that represented the people—and the right of any white freeman of voting age to vote was already very broadminded when compared to the rest of the world—their intention was to set up an administration that would limit how much citizens could directly participate in national government. Many of the Founding Fathers advocated strict limitations and checks on the "democratic parts" of the Constitution, and almost all of them envisioned a nation ruled by propertied gentlemen.

At one stage, delegate Alexander Hamilton suggested that members of the Senate and the president be elected for life and given absolute power over the states. And following George Washington's rather grand ceremonial inauguration, Congress actually considered altering his title to the more impressive-sounding "His Highness," "His Mightiness," or "His Supremacy," until they backtracked to the less majestic-sounding "President."

In the end, the delegates made one concession to democracy by allowing members of the House of Representatives to be elected by the people (the "people" being white, male property owners). Members of the Senate, however, would be elected by the state legislature, as would the presidency. (It wasn't until 1913 that senators would be elected by popular vote, and we still have the Electoral College today.)

The word democracy continued to be avoided decades after 1787. Thomas Jefferson didn't include it in any public addresses as president, and it wasn't until the twentieth century—after Woodrow Wilson became the first president to do so in a public statement during World War I—that U.S. politicians generally referred to the nation as a democracy.

Since the adoption of the Constitution, a further twenty-seven amendments have broadened the electorate and led to the democratization of U.S. politics. These amendments have largely dismantled the limitations specifically incorporated by the Founding Fathers, whose ideas about political representation were mainly rooted in the colonial past.

His Mightiness
King George

MINI MYTH

THE UNITED STATES OF GERMANY

It is frequently stated with conviction that Congress considered making German the official language of America, a plan that was rejected by just one vote. This is, however, a myth, as no such proposal was ever considered by any legislative body of the U.S. government. Indeed, around ninety percent of the United States' 3.9 million inhabitants spoke English. In 1795, the House of Representatives briefly considered a proposal that all laws and regulations be published in English and German (for the benefit of German citizens who could not speak English). It was never a popular motion, and a vote to adjourn and sit again on the recommendation was rejected by one vote. A month later, it was again raised in the House of Representatives and was immediately and resoundingly rejected. Other similar myths include that the writer Kingsley Amis claimed that Congress voted on establishing Ancient Greek and then an American Indian language, the official language of America—again, not true.

The "Iron Chancellor" Otto von Bismarck: Ruthless, war-mongering conservative and dogmatic ideologue.

Prussian-born Otto von Bismarck is considered the founder of the German Empire, a man who from 1862 to 1890 shaped the fortunes of Germany, first as Minister-President of Prussia and then as Chancellor of the newly established German Empire. For decades after his death in 1898, Bismarck was venerated as a national hero, the "most German of all Germans." But when his image was used to legitimize the far-right politics that came to plague Germany in the 1930s and 1940s, Bismarck's legacy took a real battering and led to the demonization of him as a ruthless, ultra-conservative despot, who paved the way for the Nazi regime.

Having achieved a series of Prussian victories in Europe, Bismarck secured in 1871 the political unification of German states and, with the European power balance radically altered, skillfully maintained peace through a series of European alliances. At home, he set up a national currency and initiated a common code of German law, while also implementing a number of laws designed to severely limit the influence of the left-wing Social Democratic Party and the Catholic Church.

Although always a staunch conservative and opponent of liberalism, Bismarck was not a dogmatic ideologue, nor was he fixated on war in Europe. Indeed, in foreign affairs, he developed into a master of diplomacy, and the conduct of foreign affairs became one of his main preoccupations throughout his chancellorship. He purposely *avoided* war by maintaining an elaborate and constantly shifting system of political alliances in Europe that were aimed at isolating France (which remained a bitter enemy of Germany). At home, his intent was to build a powerful German Reich (Empire) and develop a national consciousness, and while he attacked Catholicism and Socialism in pursuit of this, he did personally reject anti-Semitism and viewed radical nationalism as a threat to the peace and security of the German Empire.

After Bismarck's resignation in 1890 and death in 1898, conservatives and liberals alike mythologized him as the "Iron Chancellor," a ruthless promoter of the policy of "Blood and Iron," referring to his speech of 1862: "Not by speeches and majority decisions are the great questions of the day decided—that was the great error of 1848 and 1849—but by iron and blood." As Kaiser Wilhelm II's popularity declined during the 1920s, Bismarck was increasingly revered as the man who had laid the foundations of Germany's "greatness," whose strong leadership contrasted sharply with the weakness of parliamentary rule. He was to become one of the most popular German statesmen of all time.

As Robert Gerwarth describes in *The Bismarck Myth*, the myth built up around Bismarck was useful for future leaders and politicians in Germany, but it would lead to a false image of who he really was and what he did for his country.

Kaiser Wilhelm II first used Bismarck's reputation to justify Germany's expansionist policies overseas

REALITY CHECK
A COMPLEX CHARACTER

The crude stereotype of Bismarck as a "power politician in soldier's boots" bears little relation to his more complex character. Bismarck's appearance seemed to fit the indomitable image—he usually wore his uniform in public, although he had only one very inglorious year of military service, which he did not enjoy—whereas his temperament seemed more artistic and high strung, earning him the name of "wild Bismarck" in his twenties. Later in life, he would often resort to tantrums and crying fits to get his way with his sovereign. His public speeches were not the rants of a megalomaniac but were carefully worded (they still read well today), and he delighted in using sarcasm and irony.

(although Bismarck had originally opposed the acquisition of foreign colonies, considering them too expensive) while attacking those who opposed the social order of Germany as a crime against the legacy of the Iron Chancellor. After World War I and the subsequent humiliation of the German state, Bismarck served as a reminder of what Germany had lost. Mounting dissatisfaction with the Weimer Republic, along with the

worldwide Great Depression after 1929, further inten-
sified the desire for a strong and charismatic leader, a
"second Bismarck" who could solve Germany's problems and reassert its former greatness.

The adulation of Bismarck also gave an emerging
style of right-wing politics a historical legitimacy. Adolf
Hitler evoked the memory of Bismarck and Frederick
the Great, and presented himself as the only man able
to continue their legacies, declaring in January of 1931
that "if Bismarck were to return with his political comrades, they would all stand on our side today." However,
once Hitler's regime was established in 1933, the public veneration of Bismarck faded. The Nazis could not
allow the greatness of past leaders to overshadow that
of Adolf Hitler. For this reason, as Robert Gerwarth in
History Today noted, public Bismarck celebrations were
declared illegal in Germany.

The mythologization of Bismarck (and its appropriation by future leaders) ultimately proved disastrous for Germany, although the vast disparities between Hitler—a reckless gambler and demagogue
who brought ruin to Germany—and Bismarck—a
cautious political player, but a gambler when he
needed to be—are clear. In 1944, when Germany's
defeat was imminent, Ulrich von Hassell, who had

previously not been Bismarck's greatest proponent, lamented:

> It is regrettable, what a false picture of him we ourselves have given the world—that of a power politician in soldier's boots—in our childish joy over the fact that at least someone had made Germany a name to reckon with again. In his own way he knew how to win confidence in the world; exactly the reverse of what is done today. In truth, the highest diplomacy and great moderation were his real gifts.

REALITY CHECK

BISMARCK: ADORED OR ABHORRED?

Bismarck received far more adulation after his resignation and death than he ever did as Chancellor. His shifting foreign policy and his anti-Catholicism and anti-Socialism had created distrust within the political culture of Germany. However, he abandoned his anti-Catholic stance in the 1880s, and, despite Bismarck's disapproval, the Socialists continued to flourish so that by 1914 they were the biggest party in the Reichstag. The German press expressed little grief over Bismarck's resignation, and his departure from Berlin was accompanied by cheering crowds. The novelist Theodor Fontane even wrote in a letter, "It is good fortune that we finally got rid of him."

Bolsheviks, under the charismatic leadership of Lenin, heroically stormed the Winter Palace in the October Revolution of 1917.

The October Revolution of 1917, which followed the February Revolution of the same year, saw the Bolsheviks seize power in Russia. Bolshevik Red Guards began the takeover of key buildings in Petrograd (St. Petersburg) on the night of October 24–25, 1917, and finally captured the Winter Palace, the seat of Russia's Provisional Government, the following night. "Official" histories, paintings, novels, and films have depicted the storming of the Winter Palace as part of a mass rising, in which large numbers fought fiercely to break into a heavily guarded palace, yet the reality of the Russian Revolution was far less dramatic.

Indeed, this depiction of events is, as the historian

Steve Phillips puts it in *Lenin and the Russian Revolution,* "a gross exaggeration." Much of it is based on "politically correct" accounts created by Bolshevik propagandists, whose intention was to portray the events of October 1917 as a heroic and dramatic struggle. This was reinforced by an official historical reenactment shown to 100,000 spectators on the third anniversary of the revolution. Entitled *The Storming of the Winter Palace,* it depicted a huge siege and fierce battle. Later films portrayed a similar image, significantly Sergei Eisenstein's *October: Ten Days That Shook the World,* a documentary-style movie made in 1927, which showed Bolshevik leader Lenin and thousands of Red Guards storming the palace. So authentic did this movie seem to be that for years television documentaries passed off this particular scene as actual "footage" from the revolution.

Free from official Soviet biases, Western historians have portrayed the revolution in numerous ways, and many have debunked the heroic myth of a large-scale struggle. Indeed, the real events of October were far less dramatic: by the time the Bolsheviks entered the Winter Palace, it was virtually unoccupied. Its gates were open; its administrative staff and many of its guards had fled; and the few that remained had barricaded themselves in the former private rooms of the imperial family. The provisional government had by this time little support in the city and so little power that, as Steve Phillips remarks in *Lenin and the Russian Revolution*, "it was hardly worth overthrowing."

General Knox, a British military attaché in Russia, observed the taking of the palace:

> The garrison of the Winter Palace originally consisted of about 2,000 all told . . . The garrison dwindled owing to desertions . . . No one had any stomach for fighting; and some of the ensigns even borrowed great coats of soldier pattern from any women to enable them to escape unobserved . . . At 10 p.m., a large part of the ensigns left, leaving few defenders except the ensigns of the Engineering School and the company of women. [The so-called Women's Death Battalions.]

American-born journalist and socialist John Reed also witnessed the siege and wrote in his book *Ten Days That Shook the World* (on which Eisenstein's film was based) that by 2 a.m., once Bolshevik insurgents had flooded into the building, "there was no violence done although the Junkers [students] were terrified." Such was the mammoth and heroic storming of the symbol of czardom: the Winter Palace.

Cultural depictions of Vladimir Lenin and his role in the events of October 17 have also been misrepresented. Contrary to popular belief, he did not lead the Bolshevik troops into the palace, nor did he spur on the insurgents with a string of public speeches (as depicted in films, novels, and even ballets with "fist raised, mouth tensed and a bearded chin"). On that particular day, Lenin—who, incidentally, had no beard at this time in an attempt to disguise himself from the authorities—spoke only briefly at the Second Congress and acted more as a strategist and, as Robert Service notes in *Lenin*, an "inspirer behind the scenes."

It's estimated that only six people lost their lives in Petrograd during the October Revolution, of whom none were defenders of the existing government. Unlike the February Revolution—during which roughly 1,500 people died and hundreds of thousands were out on the streets protesting—this was not a mass uprising. The Winter Palace was not "stormed" by thousands of troops, but simply walked into by a much smaller group of fairly disorganized soldiers, who faced little or no opposition.

REALITY CHECK
LEON TROTSKY: HERO OR TRAITOR?

The military force needed to overthrow the Provisional Government in Petrograd was largely orchestrated by Leon Trotsky, not Lenin. Trotsky had joined the Bolsheviks just prior to the October Revolution. As chairman of the Soviet Petrograd, he had set up the Military Revolutionary Committee, which took over the capital's garrison and city a week before the uprising, leaving just the Winter Palace holding out on the night of October 24–25. On November 10, 1918, Stalin wrote in the newspaper *Pravda*:

> All practical work in connection with the organization of the uprising was done under the immediate direction of Comrade Trotsky, the President of the Petrograd Soviet. It can be stated with certainty that the Party is indebted primarily and principally to Comrade Trotsky for the rapid going over of the garrison to the side of the Soviet and the efficient manner in which the work of the Military Revolutionary Committee was organized.

A somewhat ironic statement considering Stalin would later hound and hunt Trotsky to his death.

Christopher Columbus introduced syphilis to Europe.

It is a commonly believed that the Italian explorer Christopher Columbus introduced syphilis to Europe. Following his historic voyage to the Americas in 1492, it was thought that Columbus's crew had picked up the unfamiliar disease of syphilis from the Americas and brought it back to Europe the next year. However, recent discoveries have shown that syphilis may well have existed in Europe long before Columbus first set foot in the New World (and maybe the transmission of the disease went the other way around).

The theory of Columbus's culpability is not without foundation, though, as the earliest-known European epidemic of syphilis broke out in 1494 or 1495, soon after Columbus's return. The disease struck French troops in Naples during their invasion of Italy, and documentary evidence cites links between the French army and crewmen of the Columbus voyage. Syphilis went on to ravage Europe and led to an estimated 5 million deaths. In an era without antibiotics, it was a fearsome disease that caused serious damage to its victim's skin, joints, stomach, heart, and brain, leading to death within a few months.

In 2008, *New Scientist* magazine reported on evidence that supported the Columbus link. Findings indicated that the sexually transmitted form of syphilis had originated more recently, suggesting that Europeans could have picked up a non-venereal form of the disease, which then mutated into a more deadly, sexually transmittable form. In addition, upon examination, the venereal-causing strains of syphilis appeared to be closely related to those found in South America (where Columbus and his crew landed).

However, even more recent evidence has established the existence of syphilis in Europe long before the voyage of 1492. In east London, on the excavation site of one of the largest medieval hospitals, osteologists like Brian Connell have unearthed skeletons dating from 1200 to 1400 that show clear signs of the syphilis disease. Out of 5,387 skeletons examined, a total of twenty-five show the terrible bone damage inflicted by the condition. One skeleton belonged to a ten-year-old

child, who, experts believe, was born with the infection and whose remains showed the painful, disfigur-
ing symptoms characteristic of its later stages. Syphi-
litic lesions had caused dents in the child's skull, and
the child's canine teeth protruded at a forty-five-degree
angle. Brian Connell said, "It caused a bit of stir when
it was found because the symptoms are so obvious."

REALITY CHECK
TRUE AFFLICTIONS

Columbus's voyage to the Americas in 1492
launched an era of wide-scale contact between
the New and Old Worlds, known as "The Colum-
bian Exchange" (a term coined by historian Alfred W. Crosby). New foods and crops (including
tobacco), animals, ideas, and people (often in the
form of slaves) were exchanged, as were a host
of deadly diseases. European afflictions, which
included influenza and smallpox, decimated the
population of the Americas, and it has been estimated that between 1492 and 1650, the indigenous population of the Americas declined from 50
million to 5 million. Thus, for many people in the
Americas, Columbus kick-started a rapid decline
in population with genocidal effect.

Recent discoveries in the ruins of Pompeii also indicate the presence of syphilis in early Europe. The remains of twin children who died in the eruption of Mount Vesuvius in 79 CE have been found to show almost certainly the signs of congenital (hereditary) syphilis. Some experts believe that Hippocrates described the symptoms of venereal syphilis in ancient Greece, which means the disease may have been around over four hundred years even before the volcanic destruction of Pompeii. In addition, skeletons of monks who lived at a thirteenth- to fourteenth-century Augustinian friary in Kingston-upon-Hull in England showed bone lesions indicative of venereal syphilis.

Douglas Owsley, an anthropologist at the Smithsonian Institution, also put forward the idea that syphilis had existed in both hemispheres before 1492 but was mistaken in the medieval period for leprosy—it is simply coincidental that the mistaken leprosy symptoms flared up in virulence at the end of the fifteenth century. Other molecular geneticists have argued that it's likely syphilis emerged in Europe spontaneously, possibly from related bacteria already rife in the Old World.

Although the first known European epidemic of syphilis broke out in the immediate aftermath of

MINI MYTH

THE COLUMBUS DISCOVERY

Columbus was once thought of as the "discoverer" of America, even though the indigenous people had been there for thousands of years and the Vikings had settled there several centuries earlier. What also tends to be forgotten is that Columbus never actually set foot in North America, as his four voyages took him to the Caribbean and the coast of South America. Added to that, when he first reached Cuba, he insisted that it was part of the Asian mainland and thus named its inhabitants "indios" ("Indians").

For almost three hundred years after his voyages, Columbus was largely forgotten, until postrevolutionary Americans, in their search for heroes unconnected with the British monarchy, resurrected his memory. In the 1930s President Franklin D. Roosevelt (partly in a bid to please Italian Americans, who were important supporters of his party) revived the myth and established the Columbus Day public holiday. The spirit of Columbus ran through all Americans, Roosevelt maintained: "You are scarcely removed one generation from men and women who [. . .] sought to conquer nature for the benefit of the Nation."

Columbus's historic voyage, he was not responsible for bringing the disease to Europe. New evidence suggests syphilis had been present in Europe as early as the first century CE, and therefore the man who was once credited as being the first European to reach the Americas (another case where they got it wrong—see facing page)—and who may have instigated the exchange of a host of other diseases between the Old and New Worlds (see box on page 38)—has finally been exonerated.

The main killing sites of the Holocaust were Auschwitz and the concentration camps in Germany.

For most people around the world, the image of the Holocaust centers upon Auschwitz and the German concentration camps. These are seen as the main killing sites of the Jews in Europe—mass murder achieved on an industrial scale, largely by means of the gas chamber. Memoirs, photographs, historic books, and news footage portray the appalling images with which we are now familiar, and these now stand as testament to one of the worst atrocities of the twentieth century.

Auschwitz was built in German-occupied Poland and served as both a concentration camp and an extermination camp. It became Nazi Germany's main

REALITY CHECK

THE CAMPS

The term "concentration camp" has been used synonymously for all types of camps established by Nazi Germany, but there was a distinct difference between the *concentration* camp and the *extermination* camp. The former were set up as places of incarceration, and the latter were established for the sole purpose of industrial-scale mass murder. As Timothy Snyder in his groundbreaking book *Blood Lands* writes, "The concentration camps did kill hundreds of thousands of people at the end of the war, but they were not (in contrast to the death facilities) designed for mass killing."

extermination site by 1944, and approximately one sixth of the 5.7 million Jews killed in the Holocaust died there from February 1943 through the end of the war. And yet Auschwitz and the German concentration camps formed just one aspect of an appallingly intricate network of camps and directives designed by the Nazis to exterminate the European Jewish population and others that they deemed unfit for life.

As Timothy Snyder writes, "Mass killing in Europe

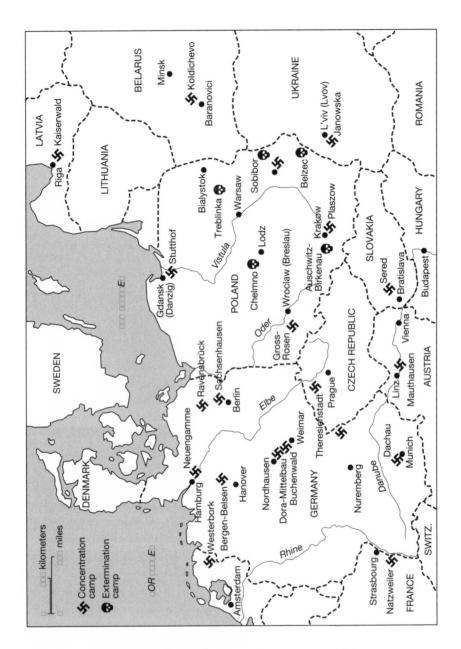

Nazi death and concentration camps

is usually associated with the Holocaust, and the Holocaust with rapid industrial killing. The image is too simple and clean." In reality, the Germans utilized a host of other primitive methods of killing across German-occupied lands (and much of it outside of the extermination camps), from starvation and forced labor to impromptu executions and mass shootings.

The German occupation of Poland in 1939 swelled the number of Jewish people under Nazi control from around 300,000 (200,000 of which were German Jews, just one percent of the German population) to around 2 million. After invasion, Polish civilians (Jewish and non-Jewish alike) were shot by the thousands by killing squads called *Einsatzgruppen*, and starting in 1940, ghettos were set up as a form of holding pens and labor camps for the Jewish population until they could be transported elsewhere. In 1940, more than 100,000 Jews were moved into the Warsaw ghetto, of which around 60,000 would die as a result of starvation or deprivation.

With Germany gaining control of the Baltic States and the western Soviet Union in 1941, a total of some 5 million Jewish people were under the control of the Reich. In the same year, Hitler gave Heinrich Himmler and Hermann Goering the order to exterminate all

Jews. By August 1941 mass shootings in areas east of
the Molotov-Ribbentrop Line (mainly eastern Poland,
Lithuania, Latvia, Estonia, and the western Soviet
States, see map on facing page) escalated to horrific
proportions. The Einsatzgruppen, often enlisting local
policemen and officials, oversaw many of the shootings, and further SS reinforcements were sent in so
that entire communities of men, women, and children
could be annihilated.

In September 1941, as an act of reprisal for a bomb-
ing that had killed occupying Germans in Kiev, all
Jews were ordered to gather at a certain point in the
city, having been given the standard lie that they were
to be resettled. Instead, they were driven to the edge
of the Babi Yar ravine and shot, each person ordered
to lie down on the long line of mounting corpses before
they themselves were gunned down. The whole process took thirty-six hours, and 33,761 people lost their
lives. By the end of 1941, around one million Jews had
been killed in this manner.

Mass shooting of civilians continued throughout
1942, and gas vans, first tested on Soviet POWs, were
also utilized throughout German-occupied lands. West
of the Molotov-Ribbentrop Line, gassing facilities
were implemented, and in Poland the extermination

camps of Bełżec, Sobibor, and Treblinka were set up. These relatively unknown camps, established to fulfill the Reinhard Action (named after Reinhard Heydrich, a Gestapo chief), were built purely for the purposes of murder (and were thus distinct from German concentration camps, such as Belsen and Dachau, which were designed primarily for slave labor and incarceration). Together with Chelmno, the Reinhard death camps went on to kill around 1.5 million Jews.

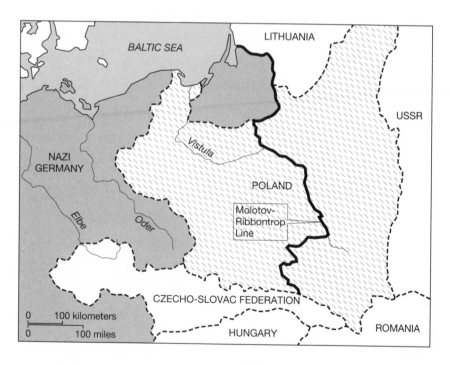

A map showing the Molotov-Ribbentrop Line, established in August 1939

Whereas around 100,000 people survived Auschwitz, virtually no one who entered the death camps of Bełżec, Sobibor, or Treblinka came out alive. The survivors of Auschwitz lived to speak of the horror of their experiences, whereas few people even knew of the existence of the Reinhard death camps because so few inmates survived. At the end of the war, American and British forces liberated German concentration camps, but they did not visit or witness the death facilities of Poland (some of which were liberated by the Red Army; others, including Bełżec, Sobibor, and Treblinka, were demolished by the Nazis). Thus little was known about some of the Reinhard extermination camps, despite the huge numbers killed there (434,508 Jews were killed at Bełżec alone).

While Auschwitz was a major site of the Holocaust, by the time it had been set up, three-quarters of the Jews killed (and almost all of the biggest Jewish communities: the Polish and Soviet Jews) had already died. The majority of Jews killed didn't see a concentration camp and the atrocities committed in Auschwitz, and the concentration camps of Nazi Germany did not represent the full horror of the Holocaust. In reality, the main killing sites were to be found in the extermination camps and across German-occupied lands, where civilians were slaughtered by the millions.

REALITY CHECK
THE BRUTALITY OF AUSCHWITZ

Most Jews who arrived at Auschwitz were gassed immediately. A minority were selected for labor and worked to exhaustion before being gassed. In addition, some 200,000 of Auschwitz's victims were not Jews—74,000 being non-Jewish Poles and 15,000 Soviets. Only at Auschwitz were all inmates tattooed with an identification number. Formerly, inmates had had their numbers sewn into their clothes, and they could be shot if they didn't remember their number. The tattooing practice began in spring 1943, by use of a large metal stamp comprising several needles forced into the upper left chest. Beginning in 1944, numbers were tattooed on to the left forearm.

WRONG

Benito Mussolini made the trains run on time.

"At least the trains ran on time under Mussolini." That is a statement frequently uttered by exasperated commuters or those trying to make the point that even brutal dictators have their good points. Unfortunately, they've fallen for Fascist propaganda, as Mussolini didn't make the trains run on time (nor did he have many good points).

The Italian rail network had fallen into a parlous state during the First World War, and improvements were made to it in the 1920s and 1930s with the electrification of lines, the enhancement of rolling stock, and the building of main routes between Rome and Naples, and between Bologna and Florence (which included the building of the second-longest tunnel in the world, opened with triumphant fanfare as "building Fascism"). Peter Neville in *Mussolini*, however, maintains that much of the groundwork for these improvements had already been put in place by the time Mussolini came to power. Mussolini's government benefited from recently established stock and relatively uncongested lines, and simply took the credit for many improvements initiated by previous administrations.

In 1936, American journalist George Seldes wrote that the trains more commonly used by tourists on the main express lines usually arrived on time but those on smaller lines were frequently late. Other testimonies from the period suggest that even the trains on the bigger lines were often delayed. The British journalist Elizabeth Wiskemann dismissed the "myth about the punctual trains . . . I traveled in a number that were late," she wrote.

The notion that Italy's trains ran on time was largely created by the propaganda machine set up by the Fascist authorities. Mussolini's key priority in government was to subjugate the hearts and minds of the Italian people, and to impress on them and the wider world the benefits of Fascism versus the doctrines of liberalism or democracy. The press, radio, films, and educational programs went into overdrive as the new government pushed through various initiatives, often dubbing reforms as "battles" (such as the marsh reclamation project, which was hailed as the "Battle for Land").

REALITY CHECK

THE ORIGINS OF EFFICIENCY

Mussolini came to power in 1922. In a bid to win over the Italian public, he drew attention to the myth of Fascist efficiency, using the Italian train services as its symbol. Addressing a stationmaster, he is quoted as saying, "We must leave exactly on time. . . . From now on everything must function to perfection." Word soon spread that Mussolini had turned Italy's dilapidated old railway system into one that was the envy of the world. Infanta Eulalia of Spain wrote in her 1925 book *Courts and Countries After the War*, "The first benefit of Benito Mussolini's direction in Italy begins to be felt when one crosses the Italian frontier and hears 'Il treno arriva orario.'" (The train is arriving on time.)

In the same way, Mussolini used the rail industry to illustrate the effectiveness of his rule. George Seldes wrote, "Official press agents and official philosophers . . . explained to the world that the running of trains was the symbol of the restoration of law and order." The new government also took care to ban the reporting of all railway accidents and delays, thereby cementing the myth of train punctuality.

This myth has outstanding durability, largely because it seems to illustrate how something good can come out of the very worst circumstances. It was a view that similarly infuriated George Seldes, who complained in 1936 about fellow countrymen holidaying in Italy who when they returned to the United States seemed to cry in unison, "Great is the Duce, the trains now run on time." And no matter how often they were told about Fascist oppression, injustice, and cruelty, they always said the same thing: "But the trains run on time."

The defeat of the Spanish Armada was a heroic victory for the English and the beginning of their supremacy of the seas.

In 1588, the vast fleet of the Spanish Armada set sail for England. At the behest of its Catholic king, Philip II, the Spanish convoy aimed to invade England, remove Elizabeth I from the throne, and thereby put an end to her piratical raids on Spanish ships and support of Protestant rebels in the Spanish-controlled Netherlands. A heroic battle ensued in which a smaller but more nimble convoy of English ships hounded and outwitted the huge Spanish fleet, eventually forcing it up the east coast of England and into the Atlantic Ocean.

The defeat of the Spanish Armada has generated a great deal of myth and confusion, much of it borne from the common perception that the battle represented a "stunning underdog" victory for the English, who were vastly "outnumbered and outgunned" by the Spanish fleet. In fact, the English had a greater number of better-equipped vessels in the water than the invading fleet, and had the erratic British weather, among other things, on their side.

As the Spanish Armada lay moored off Calais, unable to regroup with additional forces from the Low Countries, the English set fire to several old ships and sent them crashing into the Spanish fleet.

REALITY CHECK
A NUMBERS GAME

The Spanish fleet consisted of about 130 ships, most of which were troop-carrying vessels bearing 19,000 infantrymen under the command of the inexperienced Duke of Medina Sidonia. A minority of the Spanish ships, perhaps as few as thirty-five, were designed for warfare, with only nineteen of these fighting ships suited to the Atlantic waters. While the Spanish had bigger, bulkier ships, the English confronted its adversary with a greater number of vessels that were smaller but more nimble and easier to maneuver.

In the ensuing Battle of Gravelines, the English gained the upper hand, largely by means of cannons that could fire at long distances and rapidly reload when closer in. The English lost no ships, and while it's frequently claimed the Spanish fleet suffered severe damage, in reality they lost just three ships, whose seaworthiness was probably already in question. Lack of ammunition and worsening weather forced the English fleet to break off hostilities, and the Armada was able to escape, in historian Felipe Fernández-Armesto's words, "essentially intact and effectively undefeated, scotched but not killed, bloodied but unbowed."

Strong winds then forced Medina Sidonia to order the Armada—still at this point a formidable fleet of ships, capable of sea warfare—to return to Spain and Portugal via the tip of Scotland and Ireland. Storms—not English cannon—led to the sinking of numerous Spanish vessels as severe storms pushed them onto the rocky coasts of Scotland and Ireland. While it was once thought that the majority of the Spanish fleet were lost in the Atlantic waters, Fernández-Armesto maintains that only twenty-one ships were sunk and that up to five-sixths of the Spanish convoy returned home, with most of the main fighting ships intact.

These events of 1588 were almost immediately mythologized by English writers, who likened the repulse of the Spanish navy as the greatest English victory since Agincourt. The battle came to grip the national consciousness, while seeming to give strength to the Protestant cause in Europe. God himself had favored what was seen as a moral English victory over the spiritually degenerate Spanish. Commemorative medals were issued, one with the inscription, "He blew with His winds, and they were scattered."

The scale of the English victory was monumentalized as a battle of David and Goliath proportions when, as early as a few weeks after the battle, Thomas Deloney penned three ballads that described the Spanish fleet as having "great Galleazzo,/which was so huge and hye" compared to the "little Barkes" of the English. This depiction of the battle actually grew in potency so that even today the disparity between the might of the Spanish and English fleets is often overemphasized.

It's also commonly believed that the 1588 victory over the Spanish Armada saw the beginning of England's dominance over the seas. What tends to be forgotten is that the defeat of the Spanish Armada was just one of many sea and land battles fought during the

Anglo-Spanish War between 1585 and 1604. Spain recovered quickly from the 1588 confrontation, rebuilt and retooled its navy (making subsequent vessels more nimble and effective), and defeated England in several military and naval engagements over the next decade. In 1589 an English Armada launched against the Spanish navy which resulted in total failure and heavy English casualties. In 1596 and 1597 Spain launched more Armadas against the English, but adverse weather conditions continued to protect the British Isles from invasion. The Anglo-Spanish war ended in a stalemate, but Spanish possessions in Europe and the Americas remained intact while efficient convoys of Spanish ships safeguarded and even expanded its lucrative trade route of precious metals from the Americas. Spain's victories at sea continued and were not seriously reversed until the 1630s, while England's maritime strength grew slowly and haltingly. By the late 1600s, the Dutch overtook Spain as the leading sea power, and it wasn't until the mid-1700s that England truly ruled the waves.

The defeat of the Spanish Armada was in no way decisive, except in myth, and the size of the Spanish

fleet and its losses are often vastly exaggerated. In the decade following 1588, Spain strengthened its navy and bolstered its overseas possessions, whereas England failed to capitalize on her early victory, had at this point no real foothold in the Americas, and was again saved by the adverse weather—or "Protestant wind"—of the Atlantic waters, which thwarted subsequent Spanish invasion.

WRONG

Captain Scott: Intrepid Antarctic explorer and iconic British hero.

British Antarctic explorer Captain Robert Falcon Scott, once seen as the quintessential British hero beloved of schoolboys across the land, has become the subject of bitter controversy. His iconic status as intrepid explorer, whose story captured the public's imagination for some sixty years after his death in 1912, came under sustained attack in the 1970s when closer examination of his polar expedition revealed that he was in fact a "heroic bungler" who led his comrades to their deaths.

Captain Scott's ill-fated *Terra Nova* Expedition into the Antarctic set off in 1910 with the expressed objective to be the first expedition to "reach the South Pole, and to secure for the British Empire the honor of this achievement." On January 17, 1912, Scott and his four companions reached the South Pole only to discover that a Norwegian party led by Roald Amundsen had beat them there just under five weeks earlier. The 850-mile return journey—which Scott feared would be "dreadfully tiring and monotonous"—ended in disaster as one by one the team perished from a combination of frostbite, starvation, and exhaustion, with Scott himself probably dying last on or around March 29, 1912.

The frozen bodies of Scott and two other members of the team were discovered the following November,

REALITY CHECK

A "Message to the Public"

Scott's records included a "Message to the Public"—written primarily as a defense of the team's actions—that ended with the rousing words:

Had we lived, I should have had a tale to tell of the hardihood, endurance and courage of my companions which would have stirred the heart of every Englishman. These rough notes and our dead bodies must tell the tale, but surely, surely, a great rich country like ours will see that those who are dependent on us are properly provided for.

along with Scott's own letters and journals in which
he had provided a powerful and harrowing account of
the doomed expedition. Scott described how Captain
Oates, with his leg frostbitten and gangrenous, uttered
the immortal words, "I am just going outside and may
be some time," before walking into a blizzard and certain death.

News of Scott and his men's deaths, combined with
a memorial service in St. Paul's Cathedral and the publication of his diaries at the end of 1913, had a huge

impact on the British public. Although there was little interest in Scott before he left for the Antarctic (Ernest Shackleton was the preferred hero of the time), reports of his demise led to an immense outpouring of public grief as newspapers ran glowing tributes, and over the next dozen years monuments and memorials were set up around the country.

The expedition of Scott—a story driven by the virtues of endurance, stoicism, and suffering—aroused a strong nationalist spirit in the British people. The end of World War I served to increase the desire for a national hero, and the 1922 publication of *The Worst Journey in the World* by Apsley Cherry-Garrard (one of the team who had discovered the bodies of Scott and his two companions) kept the memory of Scott alive. The 1948 film release of *Scott of the Antarctic*, in which Sir John Mills portrays Scott as a classic, stiff-upper-lipped hero, further established his legendary status for years to come.

In 1979, however, Scott's heroic standing came under serious scrutiny with the publication of Roland Huntford's book *Scott and Amundsen (The Last Place on Earth)*. Having examined in detail records from both the British and Norwegian expeditions, Huntford showed how Scott had failed in even the most basic

principles of polar expedition. Not only did his lack
of food supplies lead to the dehydration and malnu-
trition of the team, but also his equipment was in-
appropriate for the extreme weather. While Amundsen's use of skis and ski champions, dogs (more than
200 and with expert dog drivers), and sleds was an
efficient combination, Scott's use of skis, dogs (just
thirty-five), ponies (which were unsuited to the extreme weather), sleds, and man-hauling (which Scott
believed was less cruel than using animals, and somehow more noble) ultimately led to the deaths of all
five men. In his extensive research, Huntford discovered Scott to be, in fact, a man who was disorganized,
inflexible, overly sentimental, and self-absorbed. The
hero was toppled.

More recent writers have sought to rescue Scott's
reputation, in particular the polar explorer Sir Ran-
ulph Fiennes who in his 2003 book *Captain Scott* vehemently dismissed Huntford's findings and described
Scott as a great historic hero. Susan Solomon, in her
research of the meteorological data in 1912, also put
forward the theory that extreme weather conditions
were to blame for Scott's failure. However Huntford's
latest book *Race for the South Pole: The Expedition Diaries
of Scott and Amundsen* contains the unedited diaries of

REALITY CHECK
THE BENEFITS OF FUR

The Norwegian team was much better prepared for the extreme weather of the Antarctic. Amundsen had learned from the Eskimos on the North-West Passage to use fur clothing and loose-fitting inner and outer garments to create air pockets and better air circulation. The British team shunned the use of fur—which was not deemed acceptable for civilized men due to its association with primitive tribes—and instead used anoraks with separate hoods.

Scott, with the cuts that had been carefully excised from earlier editions restored.

These complete journals show that Scott recognized early on that his preparations for the expedition were insufficient, that he blamed his colleagues for his own shortcomings, and that, after having discovered that Amundsen had reached the Pole before him, he clung to the hope that he could get home fast and "get the news through first." Also included (and translated for the first time into English) are the journals of Amundsen and his team companion Olav Bjaaland, which run parallel to Scott's and highlight the relative pace and position of the two expeditions on a daily basis.

On a day when the Norwegian team covered fifteen miles in six and a half hours (Amundsen cheerfully describing it as "our best day up here"), Scott's team was exhausted from having man-hauled for eleven hours, covering just four miles (Scott describing it as "a most damnably dismal day"). On another day, a blizzard forced the British team to shelter in their tent, whereas the Norwegians pushed on. The comparisons between the two team leaders reveal that one was a professional explorer and the other a gutsy but misguided amateur.

After Huntford's exhaustive review of the expedition's evidence, some would say that the Scott myth has been more or less laid to rest, but controversy around it rages on. Scott's elevation to heroic status probably says more about the British psyche than anything else: his popularity soared after the World War I, when the country yearned for a hero around whom they could unite. Had he lived he probably would have been forgotten. Instead, his failure and subsequent death bestowed upon him a kind of untouchable nobility and the British, according to Huntford, "have a perverse attraction to romantic heroes who fail rather than to Homeric ones who succeed." The backlash against Scott simply reflected a cultural shift in Britain when the heroism he represented—a kind of mindless gallantry—was no longer held in such high regard.

REALITY CHECK
A HEAVY LOAD

When Scott's sled was dug out, a geological collection weighing about forty-four pounds was discovered. Commander of the *Terra Nova* expedition ship, Edward Evans, wrote, "It seems to me extraordinary that . . . they stuck to their specimens. We dumped ours at the first big check. . . . I considered the safety of my party before the value of the records . . . apparently Scott did not."

French Revolutionary doctor Joseph Guillotin invented the guillotine.

The "humane" decapitation machine known as the guillotine has long been associated with the bloody events of the French Revolution. Adopted by the French National Assembly in 1791, the guillotine became the main official method of execution during the revolution's Reign of Terror (September 1793 to July 1794), beheading the likes of King Louis XVI, Marie Antoinette, and Maximilien Robespierre, along with thousands of French citizens. It's commonly assumed that the guillotine's namesake, Doctor Joseph-Ignace Guillotin, a French physician and secretary to the National Constituent Assembly in France, invented it.

However, the guillotine—or at least similar decapitation machines—actually predates the French Revolution by several centuries. Records dating back to around 1286 show that a similar device known as the

Halifax Gibbet was used for executions in the marketplace of Halifax in West Yorkshire, England. A machine similar to the French guillotine can also be seen in a sixteenth-century engraving entitled *The Execution of Murcod Ballagh near to Merton in Ireland 1307*, and then there is the Scottish Maiden, a machine modeled after the Halifax Gibbet that was used for execution from the mid-sixteenth century onward. In Italy, there was the *Mannaia*, and a mechanism known as a *Fallbeil* (falling axe) was also used in various German states from the seventeenth century onward.

REALITY CHECK
A POPULAR METHOD OF EXECUTION

The guillotine remained the official method of execution in France until the death penalty was abolished there in 1981. The last guillotining occurred in 1977, the last public execution (outside what is now the Palais de Justice, near Versailles) in 1939. The guillotine was also adopted as an official method of execution by both the German Empire and the subsequent Weimar Republic. Adolf Hitler utilized the mechanism, and between 1933 and 1945 about 16,500 people were executed by guillotine in Germany and Austria.

Dr. Joseph Guillotin, therefore, did not invent the device, he simply proposed to the French Legislative Assembly in 1789 that this fairly common method of decapitation should become the sole method of execution in France. Opposition to traditional forms of execution—such as hanging, burning, and beheading by sword or axe (usually reserved only for the rich and powerful)—had been growing in France, due mainly to the philosophies of the Enlightenment, which argued for a more humanitarian approach to execution, irrespective of the rank or status of the guilty party.

Dr. Guillotin's description of the machine—"This mechanism falls like thunder; the head flies off, blood spurts, the man is no more"—was, according to some accounts, met with nervous laughter, and was at first rejected by the Assembly. It wasn't until 1791 that the Assembly agreed to its use, having been convinced of its effectiveness in causing an instant and humane death, decreeing that "every person condemned to the death penalty shall have his head severed."

By this point the initiative had passed from Dr. Guillotin to Dr. Antoine Louis, the secretary of the Academy of Surgeons. A German harpsichord-maker and engineer, Tobias Schmidt, built the first prototype and tested it on animals—as well as on some stocky

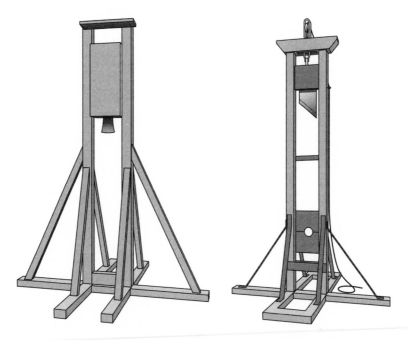

*(L) The Halifax Gibbet and (R) Schmidt's
guillotine with its beveled-edged triangular blade*

human corpses from the Bicêtre hospital outside of
Paris. The Assembly approved Schmidt's revised model,
which changed the curved blade of the original device
to a beveled-edged triangular blade. The first execution
took place on April 25, 1792, when convicted criminal
Nicolas Pelletier was beheaded in the Place de Grève.

Copies of Schmidt's guillotine were sent out beyond
Paris to all of France's new *départements*, and there
was to be no local variation. Originally known as the

louison or *louisette*, after Dr. Antoine Louis, the name gradually evolved into the more familiar *guillotine*. The macabre image of the device transfixed Europe, spawning a host of nicknames, such as "Madame Guillotine" and "the national razor."

During the Terror, thousands were sent to the guillotine. By 1795, more than 1,000 people in Paris alone had been beheaded, and by the end of the Revolution in 1799, some 16,000 people across France had been killed by decapitation. And yet, of the estimated 30,000 who died during the Terror, the vast majority were killed by other means. Many were shot, drowned, or beaten to death by mobs, as in Lyon between December 4 and 8, 1793, when hundreds of dissidents were lined up in front of open graves and shot by cannon.

REALITY CHECK
WITHOUT DISCRIMINATION

It's commonly believed that the vast majority of the guillotine's victims were members of the aristocracy. In fact, 85 percent of those killed by the guillotine were commoners, with some 1,200 members of the nobility beheaded by the device.

Despite this, the guillotine became the preeminent symbol of the revolution's terror—the swift and brutal dispenser of justice. Although new to France, it wasn't in itself a new invention, but a refinement of a device that had been in operation for hundreds of years before Dr. Guillotin was even born.

MINI MYTH

DR. GUILLOTIN

Other myths report that Dr. Guillotin was himself beheaded by the machine that bears his name. Although briefly imprisoned toward the end of the Reign of Terror, he was released in 1794 after Robespierre fell from power and lived to the ripe old age of seventy-six. His family petitioned the French government to rename the guillotine, in a bid to dissociate themselves from the butchery of the Terror. When the government refused, the Guillotin family changed their surname.

The Man in the Iron Mask was Louis XIV's brother.

"Man in the Iron Mask" was the name given to a French prisoner who was held in custody between 1669 and 1703 during the reign of King Louis XIV (1643–1715). Imprisoned in various French jails, it was said that his face was always covered either by a black velvet cloth or an iron mask, and that he was guarded by two men ready to kill him should he remove his disguise. The identity of the enigmatic figure was never revealed and has been the focus of fierce debate (and romantic speculation) ever since.

The legend of the masked prisoner has spawned countless films and novels, most famously the third installment of Alexandre Dumas's 1850 saga *The Three Musketeers*. And yet, while the story of the Man in the Iron Mask might seem like pure fabrication, documentary evidence—correspondence between prison and government officials—shows that the tale has some truth.

He's been very quiet these past few days.
I think his jaw hinge has rusted up again!

The mysterious prisoner, originally named by authorities as Eustache Dauger, was first imprisoned in 1669 at the fortress of Pignerol in Piedmont under the governorship of Bénigne Dauvergne de Saint-Mars. Louis XIV's war minister, the Marquis de Louvois, had previously written to Saint-Mars informing him of the imminent arrival of the prisoner, who should be securely guarded and threatened with death should he speak of anything other than his most immediate needs. The letter and the circumstances surrounding his captivity suggest that this man was no ordinary prisoner but someone who obviously possessed information that posed a real threat to the security of the realm or to Louvois himself.

Saint-Mars subsequently took Dauger to two other French prisons and finally in 1698 to the Bastille in Paris, where an officer of the prison, Lieutenant Etienne du Junca, wrote that Saint-Mars "brought with him, in a litter, a longtime prisoner, whom he had in custody in Pignerol, and whom he kept always masked, and whose name has not been given to me, nor recorded." In 1703 the prisoner reportedly died and was buried under the name of "Marchioly." Du Junca noted his death, referring to the deceased as "the unknown prisoner who has worn a black velvet mask since his arrival in 1698." Du Junca never referred to an iron mask, nor does any other reliable contemporary source mention one.

It was the writer and philosopher Voltaire who first claimed that the prisoner wore an iron mask—"a movable, hinged lower jaw held in place by springs"—in his *Questions sur L'Encyclopédie*, published some time between 1770 and 1772. In this first historical account of the Man in the Iron Mask, Voltaire (among others) also claimed that the prisoner was the illegitimate older brother (son of Queen Anne of Austria but not

of Louis XIII) of Louis XIV which would have complicated the line of succession.

A prisoner of royal descent could have explained the
extraordinary circumstances surrounding his captivity, which included the need to conceal his identity and
the reverence with which his jailers apparently treated
him. This theory, however, presumes that Cardinal
Mazarin (Chief Minister of France) had fathered a
child with Queen Anne, and, while the two were close,
there's no evidence to suggest any sexual impropriety
between them.

MINI MYTH

THE MYTH CONTINUED ...

Among other more fanciful suggestions, it was
rumored (admittedly about a century after the
Man in the Iron Mask's imprisonment) that the
prisoner was the king's older brother and had fathered a child during his incarceration. The child
had been sent to Corsica to be taken in by the
Bonaparte family, which conveniently made Na-
poleon Bonaparte a direct descendent of the king.
It is an appealing and fanciful notion, but no evidence exists to suggest it could actually be true.

The brother theory proved popular with Dumas and various Hollywood filmmakers (including the 1998 Leonardo DiCaprio film *The Man in the Iron Mask*) who proposed that the prisoner was the identical twin brother of Louis XIV, whose birth had been hidden. According to this theory, he was raised secretly away from court, returned years later to claim his inheritance, and was then imprisoned. A mask would have seemed a sensible precaution for a prisoner who bore a striking resemblance to the king. And yet no documentary evidence supports this theory, and one can presume it would have been impossible for the queen to conceal the birth and upbringing of a "secret" twin brother.

As speculation to the identity of the masked prisoner has broadened, among the more convincing cases have identified the Man in the Iron Mask as prisoners Charles de Batz d'Artagnan, Antonio Ercole Matthioli, or Eustace Dauger. D'Artagnan was the famously indiscreet womanizer and captain of the First Company of Musketeers, who was imprisoned in the Bastille following a quarrel with Louis XIV's minister, Louvois. The theory goes that d'Artagnan was in possession of embarrassing secrets about the king's close associates and that Louvois privately arranged for him to be imprisoned without the king's knowledge.

Prison documentation shows that the other candidates, Matthioli and Dauger, were the only two prisoners at Pignerol who could have been brought to the Bastille in 1698. Matthioli (whose name resembles the prisoner's burial name of Marchioly) was an Italian diplomat who negotiated between the Louis XIV and the Duke of Mantua in the selling of Casale Monferrato. During negotiations, Matthioli double-crossed everyone involved and was eventually seized by the French and thrown into Pignerol in 1679. However, because everyone knew about Matthioli's crimes, there would have been no need to keep his identity secret. Also, others claim that Matthioli died in 1681, not 1703.

The more likely candidate was the valet Eustace Dauger, whose master was Roux de Marsilly (Marchioly may be a misspelling of Marsilly?), a Huguenot who had tried to stir up a Protestant alliance against Louis XIV for which he was publicly tortured to death in Paris in 1669. Others have suggested that Dauger was a valet named "Danger" or "D'angers" who had botched a political assassination on behalf of the French secretary of state, however no theory has proved conclusive.

Despite the many colorful, convincing (and not

MINI MYTH

THE SKELETON IN THE CLOSET

The myth of the iron mask took on symbolic importance during the upheavals of the French Revolution. The masked prisoner, incarcerated for unknown reasons for thirty years, symbolized the tyranny of an increasingly unpopular monarchy. When the Bastille was stormed in 1789, rumors circulated (and rumor it remained) that a skeleton was found hidden in the bowels of the prison, chained to a wall with an iron mask on its skull.

so convincing) theories put forward, there is still no definitive answer to the Man in the Iron Mask's true identity, though it's safe to say the idea he was Louis XIV's brother—and that the mask was iron—are without much foundation. The secrecy surrounding the unknown prisoner has bred a huge amount of speculation and romantic fancy, creating a myth far more spectacular than the reality. It's a legend that has continued to grip the public imagination, a story riddled with mystery that has in the process generated some of the very worst—but nonetheless entertaining— examples of how they got it wrong.

Australia was established purely as a penal colony, a dumping ground for Britain's convicts.

In 1788 a fleet of British ships arrived on the eastern shores of Australia. After checking out Botany Bay, where Lieutenant James Cook had landed eighteen years earlier, the fleet moved on to Port Jackson, where they established a settlement at Sydney Cove on January 26, 1788. The fleet of eleven ships carried around 1,000 settlers, 751 of whom were British convicts sentenced to "transportation"—banishment to a land halfway across the world.

Over the next eighty years around 160,000 convicts were transported to the new Australian colonies of New South Wales, Van Diemen's Land (Tasmania), and Western Australia. The traditional view is that Australia was originally established by the British government purely as a kind of dumping ground for British convicts, as corroborated by historian Norman Bartlett in 1976: "There is no evidence that either Prime Minister Pitt or any member of this cabinet thought of Botany Bay as anything more than a convenient place distant enough for the safe disposal of social waste." It was a colonial experiment that had never been tried before, nor has it since then been repeated.

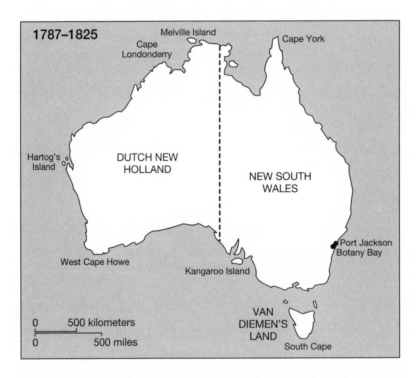

A map of the colonization of Australia during the early stages of transportation

Yet others have challenged this assumption (including Geoffrey Blainey in *The Tyranny of Distance*), partly because there appears to be no logical sense in building a prison 12,000 miles away, unless there were deeper motives behind the decision. The discovery of new artifacts has shed light on what these motives might have been. "A Proposal for Establishing a Settlement in New South Wales" is one such document, which was submitted to the government in 1783 by the American Loyalist James Matra, who had been aboard Cook's historic voyage to Botany Bay in 1770. Matra's justifications for settlement included: good soil suitable for sugar, cotton, and tobacco plantation; the potential for whaling, flax cultivation, and the availability of naval timber for the home market; and its usefulness as a trading base with China, Korea, and Japan. Matra also proposed that the colony be settled by "Americans who had remained loyal to Britain in the War of Independence" (such as himself), but this idea was ultimately rejected.

It was only in 1784, following a meeting with Lord Sydney, Home Secretary, that the proposal was amended to include "transportees [convicts] among the settlers as cultivators in their own right rather than as forced labor." Since convicts could no longer be sent to America (following the Revolutionary War), the British government had been considering transporting convicts to West Africa (a much shorter and cheaper journey), but was ultimately swayed by Matra's more comprehensive proposal.

REALITY CHECK
TRANSPORTATION

Transportation was an integral part of the English and Irish systems of punishment, and up until the Revolutionary War in America, around 1,000 criminals a year were sent to either Virginia or Maryland. British jails and hulks (makeshift floating prisons) were full to bursting with rising numbers of criminals (due to an increased population), and transportation helped to relieve the pressure put on the British prisons.

A wide range of fairly minor offenses could result in transportation, and a number of the convicts sent in the early transports to Australia had only seven-year sentences. (Many of the women—who made up twenty percent of the first convict settlers—were first-time offenders.) Had the government intended the colony of Australia to be nothing other than a gulag,

one would assume that they would have sent only
the very worst convicts. Instead, a great majority of
convicts were working men and women with a range
of skills, whose seven-year sentences would provide
enough time in which to set up the infrastructure of
the colony. On later ships, convicts were also made
up of political and social nonconformists, along with
a smattering of wayward young men from the gentry and bourgeoisie classes. (Charles Dickens sent
two of his less academically gifted sons to Australia.)

It is assumed that convicts bound for Australia suffered appalling conditions (as deaths on board wouldn't have mattered to the authorities if they were simply seen as "social waste"). Yet there is evidence to show that efforts were made to ensure the convicts arrived in relatively good health. Ships were inspected for seaworthiness, which Philip Knightley notes, in *Australia: Biography of a Nation,* made "the convict voyage to Australia . . . distinctly safer than emigrant voyages either to Australia or to America."

Before transportation, many of the inmates were stripped of their vermin-infested clothes, bathed, and held for four days while being inspected by surgeons for infection, and many of the ships carried a surgeon-general whose main aim was to limit the number of deaths en route. Later ships, particularly those administered by private contractors, suffered higher death rates, although some of those deaths could have been borne from diseases previously contracted by prisoners. While life on board the ships could indeed be brutal—prisoners were generally kept below deck in chains or behind bars—many of the convicts were provided with one substantial meal a day, religious instruction, and even a daily dose of lemon juice to avoid scurvy.

Once the first convicts arrived at Botany Bay, they were not simply worked to death in a gulag-like prison, but were integrated into a system of labor in which all people, whatever their crime, were employed. Convicts formed the majority of the colony's population in the first few decades, although the first free settlers (who were given free passage, land, and provisions) also began arriving in 1793. Convicts were allocated work to suit their skills, and the unskilled were often involved in manual labor, such as road-building.

Conditions could be harsh, and discipline was strictly enforced with flogging, leg irons, or transportation to stricter penal colonies set up at Norfolk Island or Port Arthur. From 1801, some convicts were rewarded with Tickets of Leave that gave them certain freedoms, and by the 1820s few convicts served their full sentences. By the mid-1830s, only around six percent of the convict population was "locked up," the majority working for free settlers and various other authorities. Transportation finally ended in 1868, when the population in Australia stood at a very healthy one million and the colonies were able to support themselves and grow without the need for convicts.

Although the transport of convicts to Australia did

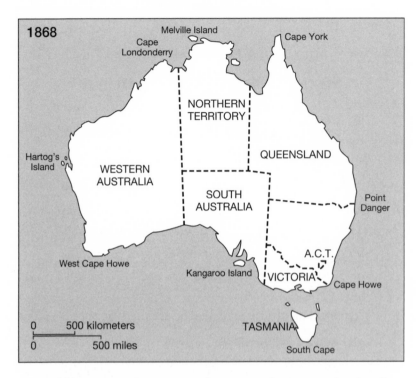

This map shows just how much Australia had changed toward the end of transportation.

relieve the pressure put upon the prison authorities of Britain, the new colony was not viewed purely as a simple dumping ground for unwanted criminals. Australia's abundant resources, strategic position, and proximity to the Far East were also motivating factors, while the convicts provided a cheap labor force who could set up the infrastructure of the colony. Conditions for many of the transported convicts were brutal, but the establishment of Australia actually proved to be one of the more humane prison experiences of the eighteenth century and a social experiment (at least for the white settlers) that resulted in a resounding success.

REALITY CHECK
NAVAL BASE POTENTIAL

The decision to colonize New South Wales was also set against the backdrop of potential war against France, Holland, and Spain. Matra showed how the colony would provide a useful naval base for attacks on Dutch possessions in the East Indies and Spanish colonies in South America and the Philippines. Over the next few decades, whenever war with Spain seemed a possibility, plans were revived to make New South Wales Britain's main naval base in the region.

President Roosevelt's New Deal saved capitalism and lifted the United States out of the Depression.

It's traditionally thought that after President Hoover did nothing to tackle the Great Depression in America, President Franklin D. Roosevelt confronted it head on, with a dazzling series of economic reforms known as the New Deal. This program, passed by Congress between 1933 and 1936, rescued American capitalism and ultimately led to greater prosperity and renewed confidence in the economy. Roosevelt was hailed as the great savior of capitalism and democracy, and a man who had restored belief and hope in America.

As Roosevelt took office in 1933, he promised a "New Deal" for the American people in the first one hundred days of his administration—a program that would provide relief for the unemployed and poor, recover the nation's economy, and reform the financial system. In a bid to stabilize the banking industry, Roosevelt closed all the banks until Congress passed the Emergency Banking Act (an act that had actually been carefully crafted by Treasury officials during Hoover's presidency). Sound banks could then open under Treasury supervision and with federal loans if needed. In June of 1933 the Federal Deposit Insurance Corporation (FDIC) was set up, which insured bank deposits of up to $2,500 and then $5,000.

To deal with deflation, the U.S. currency was taken off the gold standard (except for foreign exchange) in the early spring of 1934. Other early reforms that formed part of Roosevelt's "First New Deal" included: forcing businesses to set prices with the government and instituting regulations to prevent aggressive competition through the NRA (National Recovery Administration); setting minimum prices and wages; cutting agricultural production to raise prices through the Agricultural Adjustment Act. By 1935, the "Second New Deal" added social security, a jobs program for the unemployed, and stimulus for the growth of trade unions through the National Labor Relations Board.

The economy temporarily improved, and by 1937 industrial production exceeded pre-Depression levels of 1929, although unemployment remained at eleven percent. In autumn of 1937 the economy took another sharp downturn, and unemployment levels reached nineteen percent. The Depression lingered on, only lifting in 1941 when America joined World War II. Historian Doris Kearns Goodwin wrote, "The America over which Roosevelt presided in 1940 was in its eleventh year of depression. No decline in American history has been so deep, so lasting, so far reaching."

Roosevelt's New Deal program of "relief, recovery, and reform" ultimately failed, and, according to some economists, actually caused the depression to persist longer than it otherwise would have done. In a 2004 article for the *Journal of Political Economy*, economists Harold L. Cole and Lee E. Ohanian maintain that Roosevelt's policies prolonged the downturn by as many as seven years.

Central to Cole and Ohanian's argument was the damaging effect of the NRA: its control of wages and prices effectively created industry-wide cartels that restricted production and raised prices, which in turn distorted normal market conditions and prevented recovery. Roosevelt himself recognized this: "The American economy has become a concealed cartel system [. . .] The disappearance of price competition is one of the primary causes of the present difficulties."

REALITY CHECK
HOOVER'S FOUNDATIONS

Herbert Hoover's presidency (1929–33) coincided with the Wall Street Crash of 1929 and the ensuing Great Depression of the 1930s. Like his presidential predecessors during earlier depressions, Hoover's first instinct was to do nothing, with the hope that the "natural processes" of the economy would lead to an upturn. As the economy worsened, however, Hoover took firm action. At first he attempted to extract voluntary pledges from businesses to maintain production and employment levels, while encouraging state and municipal governments to increase public works spending. When this failed, he turned to more direct federal intervention by increasing government spending on public works (the Hoover Dam and other construction projects cost the government some $50 million), buying up surplus farm produce through the Farm Board, and endorsing legislation to establish the Reconstruction Finance Corporation (RFC). The RFC—whose purpose was to lend federal money to railroads, farmers, and financial institutions—would eventually become a key agency of Roosevelt's New Deal. Although Hoover ultimately failed to reverse the depression (or provide relief for the poor), his presidential term initiated and provided the testing ground for a more direct federal intervention.

Cole and Ohanian similarly argued that the Agricultural Adjustment Act worsened the situation by using tax revenue to pay farmers to restrict production. Not only did this put more pressure on the taxpayer, but it also led to a rise in food prices and substantial unemployment among farmworkers (affecting as many as 2 million people). Although Roosevelt's first one hundred days and intermittent radio broadcasts (known as "fireside chats") served to soothe the nation and boost public confidence, Roosevelt's critics claim that his administration led to a great deal of uncertainty and apprehension among American businessmen, discouraging much-needed long-term investment.

Additionally, Roosevelt's massive funding of government-initiated projects certainly created jobs within the public sector, but economists John Joseph Wallis and Daniel K. Benjamin argue that revenues raised for these public ventures diverted capital and jobs from the private sector. These underlying and far less evident causes actually hampered the recovery of the private sector, added to long-term unemployment levels, and had disastrous consequences for the economy.

On the surface, Roosevelt's reforms were impressive: he provided much-needed relief for the poor and those who could not help themselves; he constructed thousands of roads, schools, and other public buildings; and he "connected" with the American people with his brave series of interventionist measures. And yet many of the reforms of the New Deal served only to distort normal market conditions and prevent recovery of the private sector. Roosevelt was no savior of capitalism; some of his reforms actually shackled the natural forces of the free market system and thereby hindered the country's ability to pull itself out of depression.

Abraham Lincoln's main aim in fighting the Civil War was to free the slaves.

Abraham Lincoln is regarded as one of America's greatest presidents. He successfully led his country through the Civil War of 1861 to 1865, preserved the Union, and abolished slavery throughout the United States. It's commonly assumed that the issue of slave emancipation spurred Lincoln—to invade the southern states. It's an impressive theory, and worthy of such a fine president, but not quite true.

It took four years for the Union forces of the North to crush the Confederates of the South, and in that time Lincoln's objectives changed. At the outset of hostilities, Lincoln had two basic aims: to preserve the Union and to halt further expansion of slavery into the

REALITY CHECK

LINCOLN'S STANCE AT THE OUTSET OF WAR

Abraham Lincoln declared this in a 1858 public debate on the future of slavery:

> I am not, nor ever have been in favor of bringing about in any way the social and political equality of the white and black races, that I am not nor ever have been in favor of making voters or jurors of negroes, nor of qualifying them to hold office, nor to intermarry with white people. . . . I do not perceive that because the white man is to have the superior position the negro should be denied everything. I do not understand that because I do not want a negro woman for a slave I must necessarily want her for a wife. My understanding is that I can just let her alone.

West. But as the war continued the abolition of slavery became his new and primary motive.

Although the slave-owning states of the South were convinced that Lincoln and his victorious Republican Party were hell-bent on emancipating their slaves,

Lincoln at the outset of war was no abolitionist. At the end of his inaugural speech in March of 1861, he stressed this specific point in an attempt to pacify the Southern secessionists: "I have no purpose, directly or indirectly, to interfere with the institution of slavery in

REALITY CHECK
SOUTHERN SECESSION

After Lincoln became president in 1860, seven slave-owning states in the South seceded from the Union and formed the Confederate States of America (also known as the Confederacy), electing Jefferson Davis as their president. With the North growing in wealth and population, the secessionists feared that Lincoln and his victorious Republican Party would extend the abolition of slavery across the United States. Hostilities began in 1861 when Confederate troops fired on Union forces at Fort Sumter in South Carolina (one of only two federal properties in the South to remain in Union hands and which Lincoln, although averse to war, refused to surrender). Four more slave states joined the South's fight for independence, and war was declared between the Union forces (which included twenty mostly northern free states and five border slave states) and the Confederate army.

the States where it exists [. . .] We are not enemies but friends. We must not be enemies." His words proved futile, however, as by April 12, Confederate and Union troops were locked in battle at Fort Sumter, South Carolina, and within weeks another four Southern states had joined the Confederacy. Prior to becoming president, Lincoln had frequently spoken about his moral objections to slavery, although he often modified his stance according to the audience he was addressing. To some, he railed against the evil institution of slavery; to others he stressed the superiority of white over black. (And in his home state of Illinois he never contested the inequality of blacks who could neither vote nor testify in court against whites.)

Lincoln's views on slavery came to the fore in 1858 when he engaged with Stephen A. Douglas, senior Senator for Illinois, in a series of highly publicized debates on the future of slavery in the United States. Douglas supported the view of "popular sovereignty," that settlers in new territories should have the right to choose slavery. He tried to wreck Lincoln's chances of election by painting him as an out-and-out abolitionist. Lincoln adopted the Republican stance—slavery should be outlawed in the new territories to prevent its further spread. However, he made it clear that he had no intention to

REALITY CHECK
PRESERVATION OF THE UNION

In September 1862, Lincoln wrote a public letter to *Harper's Weekly* in which he said:

> If I could save the Union without freeing any slave I would do it, and if I could save the Union by freeing all the slaves I would do it. And if I could save it by freeing some and leaving others alone, I would also do that.

abolish slavery in the states where it already existed, nor was he a champion of racial equality. Still, at this stage Lincoln's key aim was to preserve the Union.

Eight months into the Civil War, Lincoln still looked to appease the Southern states and was adamant that the suppression of hostilities "shall not degenerate into a violent and remorseless revolutionary struggle." He even suggested to Congress that any slaves freed as result of the struggle be resettled abroad. Yet the war raged on, and events soon slipped out of Lincoln's control. With so many Southern men fighting, the slave system they left behind began to disintegrate as slaves fled to Union lines.

The untapped resources of escaped slaves proved more appealing to Lincoln, and in July 1862 Congress passed legislation to allow the enlistment of black soldiers within the army. Reconciliation with the South no longer seemed possible, and more and more Northerners aligned themselves with the abolitionists. Still, Lincoln publicly maintained that his only goal was to save the Union, and that the pursuit of war was entirely divorced from the issue of slavery.

In September 1862, Lincoln signed the Emancipation Proclamation, which declared that all slaves of the Confederate States that did not return to the Union by January 1, 1863, would be freed—3.1 million out of America's 4 million slaves would be liberated. (The bill excluded roughly 800,000 slaves from the border states that had not seceded from the Union.) Despite Lincoln's earlier intentions, the war had evolved into a revolutionary struggle in which slavery had become a key issue. Lincoln still maintained that his main goal was preservation of the Union, but he also recognized that this could now only be achieved through emancipation. In 1863, he wrote in a letter: "The use of the colored troops constitute the heaviest blow yet dealt to the Rebellion, and that at least one of these important successes could not have been achieved when it was but for the aid of black soldiers."

By the time Lincoln delivered his famous Gettysburg Address in November of 1863, his public justification for war had shifted. Invoking the principles of the Declaration of Independence, which infamously declares that all men are created equal, he now defined the Civil War as a struggle not merely for the Union but also as a new birth of freedom that would bring true equality to all of its citizens. After the passing of the Emancipation Proclamation, Lincoln lobbied Congress for a constitutional amendment outlawing slavery throughout America—this was finally passed on January 31, 1865.

Lincoln summarized the events of the war in a letter to Albert G. Hodges in 1864:

> I claim not to have controlled events, but confess plainly that events have controlled me. Now, at the end of three years' struggle the nation's condition is not what either party, or any man devised, or expected.

MINI MYTH

THE GETTYSBURG MYTH

In November 1863, Lincoln was invited to speak at a funeral service for the fallen soldiers of the Battle of Gettysburg, fought four months earlier. Posterity tells us that he scribbled his famous three-minute speech of ten sentences (now one of the most quoted speeches in history) on the back of an envelope en route to the service. This is, in truth, a myth, as Lincoln wrote the draft of his speech back in Washington and, according to David J. Eicher in *Gettysburg Battlefield*, took with him to the service five copies of the speech, none of which were written on the back of an envelope. The myth probably took hold because Lincoln's short and now legendary speech followed the two-hour (and now forgotten) speech of Massachusetts orator Edward Everett.

The United States entered World War I at the last minute and contributed little to the Allied victory.

It was (and still is) a commonly held belief that the United States contributed little to the eventual victory of the Allies. America failed to offer practical help on the Western Front and entered only to have influence over peace terms. But the reality is that America played a crucial role in the Allied war effort both before and after she sent troops to France.

At the outbreak of hostilities in 1914, President Woodrow Wilson stood firm by America's customary policy of isolation from the political affairs of Europe. America's melting-pot population of European peoples, of whom 8 million had been born in Germany, also added weight to the argument. While critics joked that Wilson was too timid to fight (shells that failed to explode were nicknamed "Wilsons" by soldiers), the president believed that the United States had a unique moral role to play, which, he maintained, would rise above the conflict and shape its eventual peace.

REALITY CHECK
AMERICAN IMPORTS

Britain relied heavily on America for artillery, ammunition, aircraft, and motor vehicles, and by 1916, thirty percent of British food was being imported from America. As the war progressed, U.S. banks made massive loans to the Allied forces, lending, by the end of the war, $10 billion to the Allies while the British blockaded much needed imports from getting into Germany. These huge loans, imports of vital goods, and the "unwritten sympathy" of the United States for the plight of Britain and her allies was of critical importance in the defeat of the Central Powers. As Gordon Corrigan maintains in his book *Mud, Blood and Poppycock*:

> American industry and American governmental tolerance were essential to the British war effort long before the United States entered the war, and while Britain might still have won the war without them, it would have taken far longer and would have taken many more lives.

Neutrality also gave a real boost to the economy of America, which in 1914 had been on the brink of recession. New markets opened up around the world, and increased demand from the warring nations boosted production and profit in the United States. In practice, however, the Allies, and not the Central Powers, benefited mostly from America's increased industrial and agricultural output, thanks largely to its vast federal reserves and to Great Britain's tightly controlled naval blockade of Germany.

During the years 1914 to 1916, U.S. exports to Great Britain and France multiplied from a value of $750 million to $2.75 billion; whereas, exports to Germany—which had fewer financial reserves than Britain and was concentrating on military expenditure—slumped from $345 million to a mere $2 million. The subsequent German shortage of vital raw materials is considered by some to have been a major contributory factor to the eventual Allied victory.

Early in 1917, the United States was finally provoked to consider military action following the publication of the Zimmermann Telegram (which revealed the threat of a German/Mexican alliance) combined with all-out submarine warfare by German U-boats against vessels of all kind, including neutral American ones. On

It says here the war was
already won before we got here.

April 6, 1917, the United States declared war on Germany, although Wilson reasserted that the agenda of the United States was different from that of the Allies: "We have no selfish ends to serve. We desire no conquest, nor dominion." Wilson saw himself as having the moral upper hand, and he also clearly sought to influence, if not dictate, eventual peace terms. In July 1917, he maintained that "England and France have not the same views with regard to the peace that we have by any means. When the war is over we can force them to our way of thinking, because by that time they will, among other things, be financially in our hands."

Committed to war, the United States rapidly set about preparing its fairly feeble military (ranked seventeenth in the world, alongside Argentina) for combat. Its army required enormous expansion, which was achieved through the conscription of some 2.8 million men, while 24 million men were registered for the draft. The training of conscripts delayed matters, as did the acute shortage of ships to take them across the Atlantic. By the end of 1917, however, around 200,000 American soldiers had been transported to Europe, and by October 1918 around 1,800,000 U.S. men were fighting on the Western Front.

The American Expeditionary Forces (the term for U.S. soldiers who participated in the conflict) saw their first major action on May 28, 1918, when American soldiers—known as "doughboys"—held the front line at Cantigny (with the help of French artillery) and eventually captured it from the Germans. In June, U.S. forces drove the Germans out of Château-Thierry, and in July and August, nine U.S. divisions helped with

the Aisne-Marne counteroffensive, recapturing the
Allied line between Reims and Soissons. At the end
of September, more than 1 million U.S. soldiers (now
formed into the First U.S. Army) drove into the Ar-
gonne Forest toward the Hindenburg Line, but their
inexperience and poor strategy brought heavy casualties, with 120,000 either dead or wounded.

By the end of October, the British Third and Fourth
Armies were over the River Selle, and all along the
lines, the Allied and American forces were advanc-
ing, while the Germans retreated. Morale among the
German forces plummeted as defeat approached, and
they were plagued with mutiny and desertion. The
Allied forces, on the other hand, attacked with what
Gordon Corrigan in *Mud, Blood and Poppycock* describes
as "a seemingly inexhaustible supply of American
manpower."

The massive autumn offensive, combined with the
economic blockade of Germany, resulted in an abrupt
end to hostilities, with the armistice coming into effect on November 11, 1918. Had the war continued
beyond 1918, the American military was poised to
grow bigger than the combined forces of the British
and French, and it was this knowledge that prompted

General Ludendorff to launch the German offensive in the spring of 1918, a decision that cost him the war.

While U.S. casualties (more than 100,000 deaths) were relatively low compared to those of the other Entente forces, they occurred in a short span of time

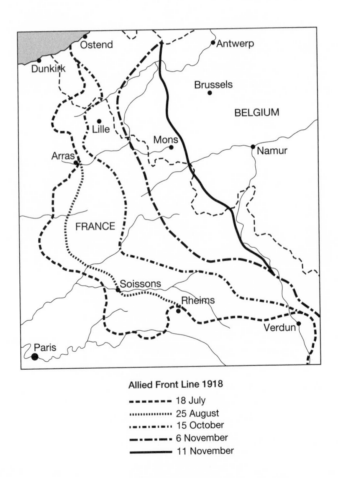

Allied Front Line 1918

- - - - - - - 18 July
.... 25 August
.—..—..—.. 15 October
—.—.—.— 6 November
————— 11 November

A map of the Western Front, 1918

and were keenly felt by the American nation, who had never before sent a mass army to a foreign war. The contribution of the Americans in the outcome of the World War I was critical. Had they not supplied vital supplies, financial loans, and, finally, their men, the war could have continued for several more grueling years and may even have swung against an Allied victory.

The Great Famine in China was the unintentional consequence of Chairman Mao's economic reforms.

During the years 1958 to 1961, the People's Republic of China underwent a series of economic and social reforms known as the Great Leap Forward. The Communist regime of Mao Zedong aimed to transform China into a modern Communist society with an economy and industrial output that would surpass that of the Soviet Union and Great Britain within fifteen years. Yet its program of agricultural and industrial reforms, which included the prohibition of private farming and radical collectivization, led to catastrophe and the loss of millions of lives from starvation and deprivation. The idea that this loss of lives was an unintentional consequence of the Great Leap Forward disregards the Maoist regime's deliberate role in exacerbating the ensuing catastrophe.

Original estimates for "excess deaths" during the Great Leap Forward ranged from 15 million to 32 million, yet the recent opening up of thousands of central and provincial documents, including secret party committee reports and public security documents, have revealed that these figures are woefully inadequate. This recent evidence suggests that at least 45 million people may have lost their lives prematurely during the years 1958 to 1962.

Frank Dikötter's book *Mao's Great Famine* draws from these new archival documents and describes how its victims were deliberately deprived of food and basic needs, and worked to death or killed as a result of the systematic violence and terror. Dikötter argues that the word "famine" fails to encompass the many ways people died, since it implies that the deaths were simply "the unintended consequence" of the state's economic reforms. Instead, there was a large element of deliberate mass killing, and of systematic neglect of the type usually associated with Stalin, Hitler, or Pol Pot, and one of the worst examples of mass murder in Chinese and world history.

Signs of famine first appeared in China in 1958; by the following year it was widespread. The new archive material shows that decisions made by the government's top officials led directly to severe food shortages and famine. Many of the regime's officials knew that people were starving to death, but those close to Mao indulged his visionary whims while others exaggerated the effectiveness of his reforms. Mao himself was aware of the famine, and in 1959 he was quoted as saying, "When there is not enough to eat people starve to death. It is better to let half of the people die so that the other half can eat their fill."

Since 1953 farmers had been forced to sell grain to the state at prices determined by the government. However, during the years 1959 and 1962, the new data shows that Mao's government increased the grain procurement quota from its usual twenty to twenty-five percent to thirty to thirty-seven percent, at a time when the average output per head was at its lowest. Some of the grain the government procured was sold back to the farmers (at an inflated price), but much of it was exported or given as foreign aid to maintain China's reputation overseas. The needs of China's countryside were deliberately disregarded in favor of the government's "export above all else" policy.

By the end of 1958, farms and households in China's countryside were organized into some 26,000 communes. Chinese society and its economy spiraled out of control as commune workers dismantled their houses to use as fertilizer, abandoned the fields to man makeshift steel furnaces (set up to achieve Mao's frenzied steel production targets), or worked on the government's mammoth and largely useless water conservation schemes—all while their families died without food. Conditions were similarly appalling for many of China's industrial and factory workers, who were forced to meet ever increasing industrial output targets, and who also suffered from famine in large numbers. By 1961, up to half of the workforce in Beijing suffered from famine edema, the swelling caused by insufficient protein intake.

Intimidation and coercion formed the foundation of Mao's regime, and anyone who questioned his policies was declared a "rightist" and punished accordingly. Coercion of workers often escalated into extreme violence, from beatings by party officials to torture. It's now estimated that at least six to eight percent (around 2.5 million) of all the famine victims were killed or died of injuries inflicted by local officials or the militia. For the smallest offense, workers could also be sent to labor camps scattered across China or to "reeducation camps" or private gulags that were attached to most communes.

While much of the evidence is still undisclosed, it is estimated that there were around 8–9 million prisoners during each year of the Great Leap Forward, of which around 3 million people died in the labor camps during the famine. Suicide rates also grew exponentially, with between 1 and 3 million people killing themselves from 1958 to 1962. Reports also show that people resorted to a variety of desperate measures to survive, from stealing and attacking granaries to abandoning their own children.

Mao's economic reforms led not just to a shortage of food but also to a shortage of all basic essentials. Approximately thirty to forty percent of China's housing was demolished, and millions of displaced peasants were left homeless, facing winters without firewood or adequate clothing (much of China's cotton was exported abroad or fed to the textile industries). The Great Leap Forward also had a disastrous impact on the natural resources of China, with the destruction of huge swathes of forest (fifty percent of all trees in some regions), while the government's irrigation schemes reduced crop fertility on farmlands and left whole regions devastated by heavy rain and typhoons.

Although Mao's famine has been known about in the West for many decades, few Westerners are aware

REALITY CHECK

THE LONG MARCH

The Long March represents a significant episode in the history of the Communist Party of China, marking the ascent to power of Mao Zedong as its leader. Official accounts tell us that between October 1934 and October 1935 the Central Red Army, under the guidance of Mao, fought its way north from Yudu in the Jiangzi province to Yan'an in the province of Shaanxi in a bid to escape from the Kuomintang (Chinese Nationalist Party). The over 80,000-strong army took 370 days to cover some 8,000 miles (12,500 kilometers) over very difficult terrain. The Long March came to seal the personal prestige of Mao, who oversaw the defeat of the Nationalist forces and its leader Chiang Kai-shek. However, there was not one Long March but a series of marches by various Communist armies. Mao did not control or even plan the march and was only told about it a couple of days beforehand. By the time the Red Army reached Yan'an, Mao was in full control, but he did not single-handedly defeat Chiang Kai-shek. Instead Kai-shek's own commanders had defected, kidnapped Kai-shek, and forced him to recognize the Communists so that they could all fight their common enemy: the Japanese.

of the scale or manner of the atrocities. As Professor Ilya Somin writes, "Chinese Communist atrocities are little-known even by comparison to those inflicted by Communists in Eastern Europe and the Soviet Union, possibly because the Chinese are more culturally distant from Westerners than are Eastern Europeans." The new archive material also confirms that the Chinese leadership was far from ignorant about the famine, and, as sinologist Roderick MacFarquhar writes, "[Mao] will be remembered as the ruler who initiated and presided over the worst man-made human catastrophe ever. His place in Chinese history is assured."

James Watt invented the steam engine.

Scottish-born mechanical engineer James Watt invented the steam engine, creating the driving force behind the Industrial Revolution. Well, yes and no. The man revered as one of the founding fathers of the Industrial Revolution (so much so that his name was used for the SI power unit, the "watt") *did* invent a type of steam engine that could be used in factories or mills, but he didn't invent the *first* steam engine.

Indeed, prior to Watt, quite a lot of work had already been done on the concept of the steam engine (which, in essence, uses boiling water to produce mechanical motion). Watt himself adapted a machine that had already been invented by Thomas Newcomen some seventy years earlier. Newcomen's atmospheric steam engine, first introduced in 1712, employed a piston and cylinder, and was used to pump water from deep coal mines in Britain and in Europe.

REALITY CHECK
THE HISTORY BEHIND THE ENGINE

The history of the steam engine is rich and varied. Before Newcomen, Thomas Savery had constructed and patented a similar water pump engine, the "Miner's Friend," by 1698. Newcomen himself based his engine on the experiments of Frenchman Denis Papin, who in 1679 invented a "steam digester," a device that extracted fats from bones in a high-pressured steam environment (the forerunner of the domestic pressure cooker). Even the ancient Greeks took a stab at making a steam engine, with a contraption called the "aeolipile," which consisted of a hollow globe that spun on its axis when steam pressure was applied through connecting pipes.

Watt's genius lay in the improvements he made to Newcomen's engine, so that it could be used in all sorts of industrial settings and not just for pumping water out of coal mines. Between 1763 and 1764 Watt, while working at Glasgow University, was asked to repair a model Newcomen engine. Noting that the engine design wasted energy by repeatedly heating and cooling the cylinder, Watt proposed that it use

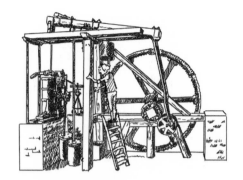

What's his name?

That was the question!

Watt.

two cylinders, one that remained hot and one, called the condenser, that remained cold and was separated from the piston chamber. This alteration radically boosted the engine's power, improved its efficiency, and saved on coal costs. Working closely with manufacturer Matthew Boulton, Watt made further alterations to the steam engine, and by 1783 he had developed a double-acting, rotating type of engine, adding a flywheel and "governor" so that the speed of the engine could be made constant. This new type of engine could be used to power the machinery of factories and mills, and by 1800, the firm Boulton & Watt

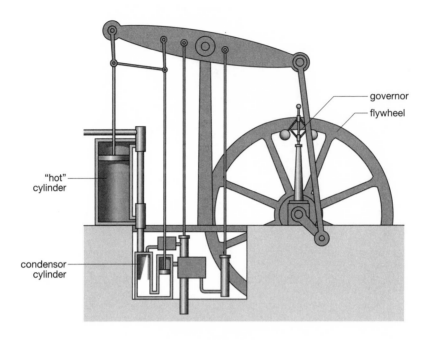

Watt's engine

had constructed some 449 engines for use in industry.

However, contrary to popular belief, the steam engine was not immediately adopted by factories in the nineteenth century; its introduction was gradual, while many manufacturers in the first half of the century continued to rely on traditional forms of power, namely water, horse, and human power. The newer industries, however—in particular the cotton trade—made great use of the steam engine, and eventually mines, waterworks, canals, and ironworks also became reliant on steam power. Later, adaptations were made to Watt's engine so that steam power could also be used in locomotives, furnaces, and steamboats. Its use also led to the development of the machine tool industry, which allowed machines to be constructed in ever-greater complexity. The real surge in the application of steam power occurred in the latter half of the nineteenth century when it was used to drive turbines that generated electricity.

While James Watt didn't develop the *first* steam engine—that achievement lay with the primitive contraption invented by the ancient Greeks—he did play a vital role in developing a type of efficient steam engine that could be used in all manner of industrial settings. And it was this development that allowed for the engine's gradual adoption across industry during the nineteenth century.

The attack on Pearl Harbor was deliberately engineered by President Roosevelt.

On the morning of December 7, 1941, the Japanese launched a ferocious and sudden airborne attack on the U.S. Pacific Fleet stationed at Pearl Harbor on the Hawaiian island of Oahu. The Japanese succeeded in sinking or badly damaging eight U.S. battleships, three destroyers, and three cruisers, while killing or wounding 3,435 servicemen. The "date which will live in infamy," as President Franklin D. Roosevelt called it, not only sparked the Pacific War, but also ensured that America would be drawn into World War II.

With a large part of the U.S. naval strength at anchor during the attack, American forces had clearly been unprepared for the assault, and rumors almost immediately circulated as to how and why the United

States had been caught off guard. Some theorists have argued that Roosevelt provoked the Japanese into attacking in a bid to maintain his own political security while also giving him just cause to enter World War II. The argument rages on and even today, conspiracy theorists argue that American officials, from the president down, had advance knowledge of Japan's intentions but were persuaded to keep silent.

Although the attack was swift and sudden, relations between the United States and Japan had been worsening for years. Since the early 1930s, the United States had become increasingly alarmed by Japan's mounting aggression against China. War in Europe led to Japan signing the Tripartite Axis Pact with Germany and Italy in September 1940. Japan then focused its military on British, French, and Dutch colonies in Southeast Asia.

The United States continued to impose heavy embargoes on Japan, and by July 1941 trade between the two countries ceased. Three months later, the moderate government in Tokyo was taken over by the more militant General Tojo ("the Razor"), who took a hard-line approach in his negotiations with the United States. American officials responded in a similar vein, announcing that the United States would only resume trade with Japan if Japanese troops were withdrawn from China and Indochina, and if Japan supported the Nationalist government in China. With neither country backing down, negotiations ended in deadlock.

In fact, the U.S. administration knew that Japan had set a deadline for a diplomatic solution, after which, if an agreement hadn't been achieved, they would go to war. U.S. cryptanalysts had cracked Japanese diplomatic codes, and U.S. decoding machines named "Magic" enabled the Americans to read confidential Japanese messages. There were thousands of these "Magic" messages that had to be deciphered, translated, and evaluated, and, even after they were, they never revealed when or where an attack was planned. The Roosevelt administration knew that an assault was imminent, but they assumed the Japanese would strike somewhere in Southeast Asia. It never occurred to them that the Japanese would target the heavily fortified island of Oahu.

American military officials also seriously underestimated the military capabilities of Japan, and wrongly assumed that Japan was unable to mount more than one naval operation at a time. U.S. officials were totally unaware that on November 26 six Japanese aircraft carriers embarked on a flight across the western Pacific toward Pearl Harbor, because the

Japanese skillfully maintained complete radio silence and avoided sea-lanes used by merchant ships.

On December 6, "Magic" machines began decoding a fourteen-part message from Tokyo to the Japanese delegation in Washington. The final part of the message apparently instructed the Japanese delegation to break off negotiations, thus hinting at war. However, there was a delay getting the translated version of the message to the Secretary of State and Chief of the U.S. General Staff so that by the time officials received it at Pearl Harbor, the attack had already begun. For decades it was thought that this was why the United States had had no prior warning of the attack; however, academics have recently argued that this last document actually didn't amount to anything as clear-cut as a declaration of war, or a severance of diplomatic relations, as the Japanese had no intention of formally declaring war or even giving prior notice to any ending of negotiation, so even if the message had arrived before the attack, it is unclear if officials would have known what it meant.

Aside from America's inability to decipher Japan's exact motives, Roosevelt himself was in no hurry for war. He knew that the United States needed more time to build up its military capacity, and he wanted to postpone hostilities with Japan for as long as possible, as he saw the war against the Nazis in Germany as more of a priority. And even when war with Japan became increasingly likely, there is evidence to show that Roosevelt wanted to avoid appearing as the aggressor. On December 6, 1941, in answer to an adviser's question as to why the United States hadn't struck first to "prevent any sort of surprise," he responded, "No, we can't do that. We are a democracy and a peaceful people."

Since the attack, the U.S. government has made nine

REALITY CHECK
HIT AND RUN

The Pearl Harbor attack was designed to be a surprise hit-and-run raid. The Japanese planned to immobilize the U.S. fleet while they conquered crucial targets in Southeast Asia. Japan lacked natural resources, and, due to the trade embargoes by the United States, she desperately needed to secure alternative supplies. Japan also hoped that destroying the U.S. Pacific Fleet would crush American morale and cause Roosevelt to vie for peace (although it ultimately had the opposite effect in uniting the country behind war against Japan).

official inquiries (the most recent in 1995), all of which have shown that there is no foundation to the argument that Roosevelt knew about the impending attack on Pearl Harbor and deliberately failed to prevent it. Rather, the inquiries have pointed to a general underestimation of Japanese capabilities as well as impaired coordination between the army and navy, and a lack of manpower in the processing of intelligence—all of which suggest human error rather than deliberate conspiracy. Indeed, Roosevelt was privy to the same information as his officials: They were warned of imminent Japanese action, but their biggest mistake was to underestimate the military capabilities of Japan.

MINI MYTH
THE YAMAMOTO QUOTE

The Japanese Admiral Isoroku Yamamoto, who devised the attack, is famously said to have told his officers, "I fear all we have done is to awaken a sleeping giant and fill him with a terrible resolve." A memorable line—which in film adaptations makes for a dramatic scene—but, sadly, there is no record that Yamamoto actually said it.

The Italian astronomer Galileo was persecuted by the Catholic Church and imprisoned in a dark cell.

The myth holds that in the seventeenth century, the Roman Catholic Church convicted the elderly scientist Galilei Galileo (1564–1642) of heresy, whereupon he was tortured and left to rot in a dark cell. The "Galileo Affair" was perceived as a battle between scientific reason and religious superstition, an encounter that laid bare the tyranny of the Catholic Church.

However, the reality is that the charges brought against Galileo were largely motivated by fellow scientists and rivals, many of whom Galileo had insulted, bullied, and dismissed in the years preceding the publication of his *Dialogue on the Two Great World Systems* (see page 133). Galileo's enemies—and there were many— set about to discredit the astronomer and successfully convinced Pope Urban VIII (a former friend and ally of Galileo) that the *Dialogue* openly mocked the Pope's views about the universe.

In 1633 Galileo was accused of heresy and forced to stand trial. During the trial it was claimed that he had been given an injunction by Cardinal Bellarmine in 1616 to refrain from promoting or teaching the heliocentric theory (see page 133). Galileo rightly insisted that he'd never received such an injunction, only a private warning from Bellarmine not to "hold" or "defend" the view that the earth moved. In Galileo's view, the *Dialogue* did not conflict with Bellarmine's warning as it presented both sides of the argument. The court eventually agreed not to press the most serious charge of "violation of an injunction" as long as Galileo pleaded guilty to the charge that the *Dialogue* gave the impression that he was defending the heliocentric theory (even though this hadn't been his intention).

In the end Galileo was convicted of the lesser charge of "vehement suspicion of heresy," the court banned the *Dialogue*, and Galileo was forced to formally recant his views. Documents detailing his conviction were widely circulated, largely at the behest of Pope Urban VIII, who was keen to make an example of him. Within these documents (as explained by Maurice A. Finocchiaro in *Galileo Goes to Jail and Other Myths About Science and Religion*), it was said that Galileo was subjected to "rigorous examination" during the interrogation process and that he was to be imprisoned for an indefinite period within the Inquisition jails in Rome. While torture was never mentioned, most assumed that "rigorous examination" implied torture and that Galileo was indeed imprisoned in what many envisaged to be a miserable and dark cell.

However, documents that were unearthed in the eighteenth and nineteenth centuries show that Galileo's "imprisonment"—with the possible exception of three days in June 1633—consisted of lodging under house arrest in a number of rather grand houses around Italy, including the Tuscan Embassy and, for a five-month period, the home of his good friend the Archbishop of Siena. Thereafter he resided at his own villa on house arrest, just outside Florence, until his death in 1642. During these times of "arrest," he spent his time working on one of his finest works, the *Discourses on Two New Sciences*.

The subsequent publication of documents relating to the trial (including minutes of an Inquisition meeting) in the late nineteenth century also reveal that it was highly unlikely that Galileo was tortured.

REALITY CHECK

GALILEO'S *DIALOGUE*

Released in 1632, Galileo's *Dialogue on the Two Great World Systems* debated the two conflicting theories on the order of the universe: the geocentric or Aristotelian view that the Earth is the center of the universe (the basis of most European thought at that time) and the heliocentric or Copernican view that the Sun is the center of the universe. In Galileo's *Dialogue*, the Copernican view, which appeared to contradict the Holy Scriptures (although Galileo was adamant that it didn't) and the "orthodox" scientific opinion of the day, ultimately won the debate. While its publication caused considerable controversy within the Italian states, Galileo considered himself a good Catholic and believed that science and religion could be reconciled. In fact, prior to the *Dialogue* he had befriended several cardinals, including the man who became Pope Urban VIII, and had dedicated his 1613 publication *Letters on Sunspots* to Pope Paul III. Indeed, prior to 1632 the Church largely accepted his science; it was the universities, steeped in the cosmology of Aristotle, who opposed him.

MINI MYTH

THE TELESCOPE

Galileo is generally credited as the inventor of the telescope. In fact, someone else came up with the idea, although sources vary on who this may have been. A popular candidate is the Dutch eyeglass-maker Hans Lippershey who in 1608 created a device consisting of two glasses in a tube that magnified distant objects. Others believe that, even earlier, Leonard Digges (c. 1520–c. 1559), an English mathematician and father of the astronomer Thomas Digges, invented the first reflecting and refracting telescopes, although political circumstances prevented him capitalizing on his invention. Galileo substantially improved Lippershey's model (even though he hadn't actually seen it) and made a telescope with three times the magnification (and later thirty times the magnification). Using this more powerful telescope, Galileo was able to develop his revolutionary theories on astronomy to include the examination of Jupiter and its orbiting four satellites (moons), which, he deduced, disproved the accepted geocentric view of cosmology.

It was rare for Inquisitors to torture defendants in Rome, and rules forbade the torture of the elderly or the sick. (Galileo was sixty-nine and suffering from arthritis and a hernia.) Strict Inquisition rules also decreed that any torture had to be put to formal vote, of which there is again no reference. The worst that may have happened to Galileo is that he was *threatened* with torture; had he been physically tortured (which generally involved tying the victim's hands behind his back and suspending them from the ceiling, often resulting in dislocation of the shoulders), it's highly unlikely he would have been well enough to have attended the rest of the trial.

Bloody Mary was a ruthless persecutor of English Protestants.

Queen Mary I or "Bloody Mary," as she is commonly known, is remembered as a religious persecutor—a childless Tudor queen who mercilessly burnt at the stake hundreds, if not thousands, of Protestants in her quest to restore Catholicism in England. Mary did execute 290 religious dissenters and Protestants, and while this was not an insignificant number, neither was it extraordinarily high compared to the brutality of the times. Mary's sister, Elizabeth I, burnt just as many Catholics, and their father Henry VIII killed off thousands more during his reign.

Mary I has remained, in the words of the historian Linda Porter, one of the "most maligned and misunderstood of all monarchs." Frequently depicted as a weak-willed Catholic bigot, her reign has always compared unfavorably with the "golden age" of Elizabeth I. As the first Queen of England, Mary was assumed to be imbued with the "feminine" traits of fierce emotion and unbridled lust. Elizabeth, however, showed more masculine traits, proclaiming that though she had the "body of a weak and feeble woman" she had the "heart and stomach of a king."

Mary's Spanish heritage (her mother was Catherine of Aragon) and marriage to the Spanish king, Philip II, further entrenched her in the world of Catholicism and provoked deep suspicion among the English populace. Her desperate and failed attempts to produce a child proved her greatest tragedy undermining her marriage and ultimately leading to Protestant succession.

And yet when Mary was crowned in 1553, there was jubilation among the populace as ballads, sermons, and poems celebrated the ascension of a warrior queen and deliverer. In securing the throne, Mary had shown considerable determination and fortitude (far removed from her supposedly weak-willed nature), mustering men and support, causing the Privy Council to switch its allegiance from the incumbent Lady Jane Grey to Mary. Again, in 1554, Mary as Queen rallied Londoners with a rousing speech and shut down Thomas Wyatt and his army of rebels who were opposed to her intended marriage to Philip II. In an attempt to pacify the country and to dampen rumors that she was selling England to Spain, Mary proclaimed that she was married to the realm first.

In July 1554, the royal marriage went ahead, whereupon Mary, who had initially shown some moderation toward her religious adversaries, pressed ahead with her plans to restore papal jurisdiction in England. In the autumn of that year, the heresy laws of the fifteenth century (which allowed for burning as a penalty) were revived, and all of Henry VIII's statutes against papal authority were repealed. Around eight hundred Protestants—including the English historian John Foxe (see page 140)—fled the country, while those who continued to defend their Protestant faith were subject to persecution under the heresy laws.

The executions began with four clergymen in February 1555 and continued with the burning of Bishops Hugh Latimer and Nicholas Ridley, as well as the Archbishop of Canterbury, Thomas Cranmer, who, despite having recanted and repudiated Protestant theology, was condemned to death. With Cardinal Reginald Pole as Archbishop of Canterbury, the burnings continued, largely in the eastern regions of England, where Protestantism was more entrenched.

The common perception is that these executions, also known as the Marian Persecutions, turned its victims into martyrs of the Protestant cause, thus influencing public opinion against Catholicism and Mary's government. Eamon Duffy in his book *Fires of Faith* argues, however, that the burnings were largely accepted by the general populace. The real cause for growing discontent with Mary was her Spanish marriage, her pro-Spanish policies, and war with France, which led to French forces seizing Calais, England's remaining foothold in mainland Europe, in January 1558. Combined with this, the years of Mary's reign were also persistently wet, which resulted in failed harvests and famine.

MINI MYTH

THE ORIGINS OF THE
BLOODY MARY MYTH

The maligning of Mary's image began as soon as her half-sister Elizabeth I took the throne in 1558, but it really gained momentum in the seventeenth century, when Protestants, who nicknamed her "Bloody Mary," used her example to highlight the dangers of Catholic rule in England. The perception of Mary as a brutal tyrant was largely shaped by two publications written by the Protestant exiles John Knox and John Foxe. Knox's *The First Blast of the Trumpet Against the Monstrous Regiment of Women*, published in 1558, attacked Mary and referred to her as a "monstrous Amazona." And John Foxe's *The Book of Martyrs*, published in 1563, "recorded in loving and gruesome detail" the lives and deaths of Mary's victims. The book went on to be a bestseller and was read almost as widely as the Bible. As Roger Lockyer in *Tudor and Stuart Britain 1471–1714* states, "Mary had given the English Protestant church its martyrs; Foxe made sure that their deeds would be an inspiration to generations of those who came after."

The reign of Mary I is now inextricably linked with the persecution of Protestants, yet in the 1550s, thousands of Protestants in the Netherlands lost their lives and far more Huguenot Protestants were burned in France (culminating in the infamous St. Bartholomew's Day Massacre of 1572 when between 5,000 and 10,000 were killed). The obsession with the Marian Persecutions also tends to overlook Mary's achievements as monarch. She improved the financial administration of government (which had been sliding toward bankruptcy during the later years of King Henry VIII's reign). She reformed the coinage; managed Parliament; and ultimately secured the throne as the first crowned Queen of England and Ireland (thereby defending the line of Tudor succession).

Mary's greatest misfortune was to die young (from fever at the age of forty-two) and childless—had she lived longer and succeeded in reestablishing Catholicism in Britain, she no doubt would have been celebrated as a valiant defender of the nation's faith. Instead, her history was written by Protestants, who bequeathed to us the image of Mary as a ruthless persecutor of Protestants, an image that, however distorted, is still as prevalent today as it was in the days of John Foxe.

St. Patrick was Irish.

On St. Patrick's Day (March 17), millions of people around the world dress in green, don a shamrock, and celebrate all things Irish. As the patron saint of Ireland, the fifth-century apostle St. Patrick is seen as the very embodiment of Ireland and a true Irishman in every sense. However, he was in fact born in Britain; his original name was Maewyn Succat; and he didn't go to Ireland until the age of sixteen.

Two letters written in Latin, which are generally accepted to have been written by St. Patrick, provide the details we have on the apostle's life. He was born in (or around) 387 CE to a Romanized British family in, as he tells us in his *Confessio*, the settlement of "Bannavem Taburniae." This place name now does not exist on any current map of Britain, although locations suggested include Kilpatrick in Scotland, Banwen in Wales, and somewhere between Chester and the Solway Firth.

Patrick tells us that when he was sixteen he was captured by a gang of Irish pirates and taken as a slave to Ireland. There he spent six years herding sheep and tending pigs, again at an uncertain location—possibly in County Mayo or at Slemish Mountain in County Antrim. It was during these years that he turned with fervor to his faith and spent much of his time praying.

Patrick finally managed to escape captivity in Ireland by stowing away on a boat bound for Britain, and he eventually returned to live with his parents. Having been trained and ordained a priest, he returned to Ireland in 432 CE, inspired, as he wrote in *Confessio*, by a dream in which a voice that said to him (as translated from the Latin), "We beg you, holy youth, that you shall come and shall walk again among us."

He answered his calling and returned to Ireland as the country's second bishop. Now known as Patrick, he went on to baptize and convert thousands of people and bring the message of Christianity to much of Ireland. However, Patrick was not Ireland's first Christian missionary, as there were already other Christian believers in the country. Ireland had strong trading links with the Roman Empire and therefore would have been touched by Christianity in some way. In the fifth century, Pope Celestine I is said to have sent Ireland its first bishop, Palladius, and he may well have joined other clerics already administering to existing Christian communities in Ireland.

Following a fairly turbulent life as a bishop in Ireland (during which time he was robbed, arrested, and accused of financial impropriety), Patrick died (it is said) on March 17, 461 CE (although 493 CE has also been suggested). Thereon he was largely forgotten, although during the twelfth century mythology slowly grew around the legend of Patrick. Centuries later, as part of the widespread veneration of saints and missionaries—particularly Irish ones—who continued to spread Christianity and monastic and scholarly

MINI MYTH

ST. PATRICK AND THE SNAKES

Another popular myth associated with St. Patrick is that he freed Ireland from snakes by driving them into the sea after they began attacking him during a forty-day fast. According to the *Concise Oxford Dictionary of the Christian Church*, "he stood on a hill . . . and used a staff to herd the slithering creatures into the sea, banishing them for eternity." The problem with this myth is that snakes have never existed in Ireland, and still don't today. Following the last Ice Age 10,000 years ago, snakes returned to northern and western Europe, but never returned to Ireland as it was protected by the surrounding seas. (In fact, Ireland, along with Greenland, Iceland, New Zealand, and Antarctica, are the few places in the world which are completely snake-free zones.) The story has a more metaphorical meaning: snakes often symbolize evil and the driving out of the snakes more likely refers to Patrick's mission to rid Ireland of its evil, pagan influence.

traditions when the rest of Europe had fallen to warring tribes, Patrick was honored as the patron saint of Ireland.

Saint Patrick's feast day has been observed in Ireland as a fairly minor religious holiday for centuries. In the main, it's Irish immigrants living abroad, particularly those living in the United States, who, in a bid to reconnect with their Irish roots, have turned St. Patrick's Day into a much bigger celebration. The first St. Patrick's Day parades were held by Irish soldiers fighting in the Revolutionary War, and hundreds of parades and celebrations are now held in the United States, Canada, Australia, and across the world. In Ireland, St. Patrick's Day has also become more commercialized (up until the 1970s all pubs in Ireland were closed on St. Patrick Day), and hundreds of thousands of people now take part in Dublin's multiday celebrations.

So the truth is out: St. Patrick was not Irish, nor did he alone establish Christianity in Ireland. But perhaps the old adage that "everybody's Irish on St. Patrick's Day" applies just as much to St. Patrick as it does to those celebrating his memory.

Roman gladiators fought to the death.

It's a popular belief that the citizens of Ancient Rome liked to spend much of their year perched high up in the amphitheater, where they could revel in the bloodbath of the gladiatorial contests below. Gladiators fighting to the death or slaying an array of exotic animals provided a captivating spectacle. It also created an image of Roman brutality that still holds great fascination today in movies, books, and television shows on premium channels featuring scantily clad actors whose togas surely would not have been considered practical attire in ancient times. Yet the reality of gladiatorial contests was quite different from this common perception. Combat developed during the Roman period as part of a funeral rite and eventually became a highly organized public spectacle in which the death of the gladiator was no longer the ultimate goal.

Bring on the gladiators.

Indeed, much of what we know (or think we know) about gladiatorial combat is mired in misconception that was shaped in relatively recent years by the Hollywood blockbusters *Spartacus* (1960) and *Gladiator* (2000). It's an area of history often subject to vivid imaginings and supposition as little survives from the period to tell us exactly what happened during gladiatorial games. Contemporary accounts, written histories, Roman mosaics, and other pictorial images give some background clues, but written descriptions of actual gladiatorial matches are few and far between (see box on facing page).

REALITY CHECK
LIBER SPECTACULORUM

The only surviving detailed account of a gladiatorial battle comes from the Roman poet Martial. The poem, from his *Liber Spectaculorum*, describes a battle between the gladiators Verus and Priscus held in 80 CE, on the first day of Emperor Titus's games at the Colosseum in Rome. It's an evenly matched fight ("equal they fought, equal they yielded"). Both are declared victors, and both are granted the *rudis*, or wooden sword, by Titus, which signified their freedom.

The gladiatorial games, during which armed combatants ("gladiators," meaning "swordsmen") fought against each other, evolved from an Etruscan funeral rite in which the dead were honored with offerings of blood. These *munera*, as they were called, were believed to have been introduced to Rome in 216 BCE, when the sons of Marcus Lepidus honored their deceased father by setting three pairs of gladiators against each other in a fight to the death. In 46 BCE, Julius Caesar, having commemorated his father in a similar way, hosted a munera at the tomb of his daughter Julia, who had died in childhood eight years previously. An elaborate affair, large numbers were killed—including several of Caesar's own soldiers.

Gradually the munera became separated from the funerary context and evolved into a very public display of wealth and prestige by the aristocratic elite. In Rome the emperors eventually assumed control of the "gladiatorial games," and by the time of Trajan (98 CE to 117 CE), military victories were celebrated by as many as 5,000 pairs of gladiators. By the end of the second century CE, writer Tertullian in *De spectaculis* (part XII) complained that "this class of public entertainment has passed from being a compliment to the dead to being a compliment to the living."

For these more public spectacles, gladiators were no longer required to fight to the death (unlike the more private munera, for which death was a necessary outcome). The running order of events at these gladiatorial games often followed a standard formula: animal fights or hunts in the morning (usually fought not by gladiators as such but by condemned criminals known as *bestiarii* or by trained animal hunters known as *venatores*), then a variety of special features, which could include the execution of criminals and "comedy fights," followed by the gladiatorial contests in the afternoon.

The main sponsor of the games was known as the "editor," and many matches employed a senior referee and an assistant (as depicted in many mosaics featuring gladiatorial combat). These referees would keep a close eye on the proceedings, while deferring to the judgment of the editor, who would decide the fate of a defeated combatant (based largely on the mood of the crowd). While the exact details surrounding the rules of combats are lost, the existence of these mediators suggests the matches were well organized and subject to complex regulations.

It's thought that the combatants, rather than fighting each other in a great free-for-all, more commonly fought in evenly matched pairs, with one style of gladiator (there were seven categories of fighters) pitted against another style. A *retarius* gladiator, for example, who was lightly armed with a net and trident, might be paired with the more heavily armed, but less mobile, *secutor*. These gladiators—who were mostly slaves, prisoners of war, and the occasional free-born volunteer—received rigorous training, lots of food and medical attention, and were thus viewed by their trainers (*lanistae*) as valuable commodities, not to be dispatched lightly. The top gladiators might fight only two or three times a year, and some gladiators survived to reach retirement. If a gladiator died during combat, a *lanista* might well expect the game's editor to pay heavy compensation, thus making any

MINI MYTH
THUMBS UP / THUMBS DOWN

It's popularly thought that Roman spectators would decide the fate of a defeated gladiator by showing either a "thumbs down" for death, or "thumbs up" if they thought he should be spared. However, one of the only direct references to this hand gesture comes from the Roman poet Juvenal, who wrote in his *Satire III* that the Roman mob indicated who should be slain by "a turn of the thumb." The problem is we don't know which way the thumb was turned: some historians claim it was turned upward, others downward or in a sideways motion. And there is little evidence to corroborate Juvenal's reference (Martial wrote that a crowd appealed for mercy by waving a handkerchief or by shouting). If a gladiator wished to surrender, it's thought that he would lay down his arms and raise his index finger, usually his left one, as a gesture of asking for mercy to the crowd. The referee would then stop the match and would refer to the editor or emperor if a final decision needed to be made.

gladiatorial bloodbath an expensive outcome for the game organizers.

It's been estimated that during the first century CE, there was a ninety percent survival rate among gladiators. In a society where life and death hung in precarious balance, where half of Rome's population would die before their twentieth birthday, the professional gladiator, fighting for the entertainment of the masses, would fare much better than many of his spectators. So, while death was a certainty for any condemned criminals who entered the arena, few bouts—probably a maximum of one in ten—ended in the death of a gladiator.

The idea that Roman gladiators fought to the death has been propounded throughout history, and has been more recently popularized with the release of gladiator-themed Hollywood blockbusters. Yet, while historical evidence of actual combat is scarce, what does survive challenges the common perception that gladiators fought to the death.

Vichy France leader Philippe Pétain tried to save Jews from the Holocaust.

Set up after the German invasion of France, the Vichy Government of 1940 to 1945 was headed by World War I veteran Philippe Pétain. As a collaborative government, Pétain's administration maintained legal authority over roughly two-fifths of France, with the capital situated in the central spa town of Vichy. By 1939 France had the second largest population of Jews in Europe (some 330,000), half of whom were European refugees who had fled to France in the hope that they would be protected from persecution. However, between 1942 and 1945 the Vichy regime transported nearly 76,000 Jewish refugees and French citizens to Nazi concentration camps. Pétain always claimed he opposed their deportation and that he had in fact tried everything he could to stop it, but increasing evidence has come to light to suggest he and other Vichy officials were fully complicit in the deportation.

The image of Pétain as reluctant Nazi collaborator and innocent bystander during the Holocaust persisted in France for more than half a century, much of it borne from a general unwillingness to revisit the "dark years" of the Vichy regime. For decades, common perception had it that the Vichy government shielded the French from the worst evils of Nazi rule, an argument reinforced by Robert Aron in his major 1954 historical work *Histoire de Vichy*. The popular view was that Pétain, the great hero of World War I's Battle of Verdun, skillfully played off the Germans while in secret negotiations with the Allies, and it was his pro-Nazi Prime Minister Pierre Laval ("the Germans' man") who was largely to blame for the anti-Jewish sentiment within Vichy.

But in 1972 the publication of a book by American historian Robert Paxton, *Vichy France: Old Guard and New Order 1940–1944*, demolished this image of the Vichy regime, reigniting a bitter debate in France. Having examined both French and German records, Paxton showed that Pétain wasn't playing any sort of double game with the Nazis, that the Germans in fact gave Pétain enormous freedom of action, and that the Vichy regime's ultimate aim was to establish itself within the Nazi new order of France.

In 1981 another book by Paxton and Michael Marrus, *Vichy France and the Jews*, argued that anti-Semitism was at the very heart of the Vichy regime and that Vichy officials and police were directly involved in the rounding up of Jews to the east. Six years later, in 1987, the bringing to trial of Klaus Barbie, the German chief of the Gestapo in Lyon, further highlighted

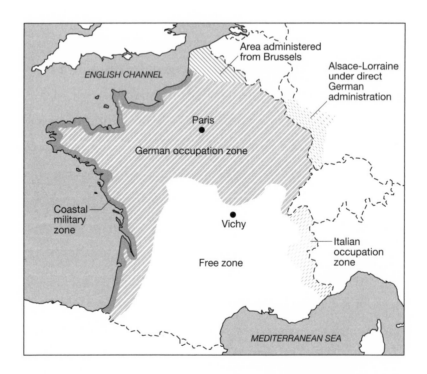

A map of Vichy France, 1940 to 1944

the involvement of the Vichy regime in the Holocaust, as did the jailing of one of his French aides, Paul Touvier, in 1992.

It wasn't until 1995 that Jacques Chirac, who had succeeded ex-Vichy official François Mitterrand as president of France, apologized to the Jews for "the criminal insanity of the occupying power [that] was assisted by [the] French State," breaking with the long-standing conviction that Vichy was an illegal aberration that did not represent France. And the 1998 imprisonment of ex-cabinet minister Maurice Papon for his involvement in the deportation of Jews from Bordeaux finally established the complicity of the French in the Holocaust. Since then, France has paid compensation and returned property to survivors, and opened up a wealth of previously undisclosed archives relating to the Vichy government.

In 2010, the anonymous donation of a previously unseen document to the Holocaust Memorial Museum in Paris provided an unsettling insight into the first anti-Jewish legislation of the Vichy regime. Enacted in October 1940, the statute excluded Jews from a wide range of professions, leading to the confiscation of Jewish property and a broad system of anti-Semitic measures that later facilitated the holding and deportation of Jews to Nazi death camps. Throughout 1940 and 1941 more than 40,000 refugees were held in French concentration camps, while in 1941 French police began mass arrests of Jewish people. In August 1942 Vichy police hunted down Jewish refugees, seized Jewish families from their homes, and transported around 11,000 men, women, and children to the Drancy internment camp outside Paris (a main transit center for Auschwitz). During 1942, Vichy officials sent 41,951 Jews to Germany, then another 31,889 in 1943 and 1944. Out of 75,721 Jewish deportees, fewer than 2,000 survived.

Part of the draft bill for the 1940 anti-Jewish legislation, the newly donated document contained numerous annotations that experts have authenticated as Pétain's own handwriting. The document reveals that the statute originally excluded the descendants of Jews who were born French or naturalized before 1860. Pétain's alleged amendments crossed out the exclusion clause and made the statute applicable to all Jews, both foreign and French, and barred them from a wider range of professions.

The historian and lawyer Serge Klarsfeld, who unveiled the document, said, "This document establishes Pétain's decisive role in drawing up this position in the most aggressive way," indicating that Laval was not solely responsible for the regime's anti-Semitic measures. It also destroys the still widely held myth that Pétain and the Vichy regime sought to protect French Jews over refugee Jews (as at least double the percentage of non-French Jews died between 1940 and 1944 as compared to 15 percent of French Jews).

Right from the outset of the Vichy regime, it's clear that Pétain never had any intention to save Jews, French or otherwise, from deportation. Moreover, as Klarsfeld says, "Pétain not only intervened to push legislation against Jews further than proposed, but created an entire anti-Semitic outlook and framework that in 1940 was even harsher than what the Germans had adopted." The unveiling of this document marks another major step in history's reexamination of Pétain, further demolishing the now dwindling argument that he strove to protect Jews living in France from the Holocaust.

WRONG

Thanksgiving Day harks back to the "First Thanksgiving" given by Plymouth settlers in 1621.

Thanksgiving Day is a time for families to feast, watch football, take in a parade, and to give thanks, of course, for the many blessings of the past year. The common assumption is that the celebration owes its origins to the "first Thanksgiving" of 1621, when New England settlers in Plymouth gave thanks to God for a bountiful harvest following a particularly harsh winter (during which 46 of the 102 pilgrims had died). According to the only contemporary account we have of the event, written by the Pilgrim leader Edward Winslow in *Mourt's Relation*, the feasting and recreation took place over three days and included the participation of ninety Wampanoag Indians and their chief, Massasoit, who donated five deer to the celebrations.

The origins of Thanksgiving, however, are not quite so clear-cut and, like many commonly accepted traditions, appear to be a blurring of myth and fact. To begin with, the events of 1621 did not technically constitute the "first Thanksgiving." Celebrations to give thanks for a good harvest or any kind of good fortune is a ritual common to cultures all around the world, and they were certainly performed in America before 1621. Indeed, for millennia Native Americans have performed rituals giving thanks for all the gifts of life. Settlers in Newfoundland in 1578 probably held one of the first colonial services

You realize this means we'll have to invite them back to our place.

REALITY CHECK
A Cover-Up Job

Neither the Wampanoag Indians nor the British settlers referred to the harvest feast of 1621 as a "Thanksgiving." Some theorists have suggested that the three-day event was more likely a series of political meetings to secure a military alliance. Neither side trusted the other fully, and the arrival of ninety American Indians (all of them men) following the sound of gunshot from the British hunters was probably an act of military precaution. For many Native Americans, Thanksgiving represents the conquest and genocide of their people, and some have accused the United States of fabricating the Thanksgiving story in a bid to whitewash the injustice caused to the indigenous peoples of America.

of Thanksgiving (a combination of age-old traditions of harvest festivals and religious services), as had the Spanish settlers in Florida some years before that.

The idea of holding a Thanksgiving holiday did start to gain more popularity following the feast of 1621. In 1623, after the Plymouth settlers' prayers during a drought were followed by some much-needed rain, they held a Thanksgiving service even greater than the ceremony they'd held two years previously. Governor Bradford proclaimed it a day of Thanksgiving in the form of prayers and thanks to God. From then on, the occasional day of Thanksgiving, in the form of prayers for any kind of auspicious event, was held—albeit sporadically and at a very local level.

It wasn't until 1777 that regular Thanksgiving ceremonies took place, when the Continental Congress declared the first national day of Thanksgiving (largely in response to the defeat of the British at Saratoga during the Revolutionary War). Later in the century, various congressional representatives pushed for the adoption of a legal holiday of Thanksgiving, but questions were raised over its legitimacy and date. Presidents Washington, Adams, and Monroe issued further proclamations for a day of national Thanksgiving, although presidents Jefferson and Jackson objected to the national government's involvement in a religious observance. By the 1850s most states celebrated Thanksgiving but often on different dates.

President Abraham Lincoln, in the middle of the Civil War, was the first to declare Thanksgiving a national holiday in the hope that it might unite a war-torn country. The date Lincoln chose was August 6, although it was moved arbitrarily to the last Thursday of November the following year. (And here it has roughly remained, bar a two-year interlude during the Depression when Franklin D. Roosevelt brought it forward by a week in a bid to lengthen the Christmas shopping season.)

It wasn't until the mid-nineteenth century that Thanksgiving became particularly associated with the harvest celebration of 1621. The establishment of the national holiday of Thanksgiving came just after a renewed interest in the Pilgrims and the Wampanoag, caused partly by the recovery of the lost manuscript *Of Plimoth Plantation* by Governor Bradford (a retrospective journal describing the early days of the Plymouth colony) in 1855, along with Henry Wadsworth Longfellow's poem *The Courtship of Miles Standish* in 1858. The idea was also imbedded by the antiquarian Alexander Young, who commented in 1841 when he published the pilgrim leader Edward Winslow's previously lost account of the harvest meal of 1621, "This was the first Thanksgiving, the harvest festival of New England."

By the beginning of the twentieth century, the harvest meal of 1621 had begun to be taught to school children as a lesson on being good citizens. (It is still lovingly recreated and sung about in school plays and pageants across the nation.) At the same time, the holiday moved away from its religious roots, enabling immigrants in the United States to share in its tradition, while the more secular traditions of parades and sporting events grew in number.

MINI MYTH
TURKEY DINNER

The modern-day Thanksgiving meal of turkey, sweet potato pie, corn bread, mashed potatoes, cranberry sauce, and pumpkin pie is said to resemble the harvest meal of 1621. However, turkey was not specifically mentioned in Edward Winslow's account, who wrote, ". . . Our governor sent four men on fowling. . . . They four in one day killed as much fowl as, with a little help beside, served the company almost a week." While the settlers and Wampanoag ate wild turkey, at that time of year (the harvest meal was held at some point between the beginning of October and beginning of November), it's likely they hunted waterfowl, such as ducks or geese. The 1621 feast also included venison—as Winslow mentions the Wampanoag donating five deer—and it's doubtful the settlers would have had the sugar they needed to make cranberry sauce or pumpkin pie (although they may well have had pumpkins).

Thanksgiving Day still has a deep association with the events of 1621 and has come to symbolize intercultural peace and the sanctity of home, family, and the community. But it wasn't until the late nineteenth century that this association really took root. The combination of Lincoln's declaration of Thanksgiving as a national holiday and the rediscovery of lost manuscripts relating to the Plymouth settlers consolidated the idea that Thanksgiving harked back to the harvest meal of 1621, though celebrations of thanks have existed for as long ago as there were things to be thankful for.

Oliver Cromwell: Man of the people and common-man's hero.

In 1653, Oliver Cromwell (1599–1658) rose from provincial obscurity to become Lord Protector of England, Scotland, and Ireland, and ruler of the nation's republican Commonwealth. A revolutionary figure who rallied for the abolition of monarchy, Cromwell has gained the reputation of a common-man's hero, a man who, in opposition to aristocratic and monarchial oppression, rose from nowhere to become the most powerful man in England. And yet Cromwell hailed from aristocratic stock, and his ancestry was anything but common.

In 1599, Cromwell was born into a considerably wealthy family in Huntingdonshire, England. Several members of his family had served as JPs (Justices of the Peace) or MPs (Members of Parliament) for the county. While Cromwell's family had no hereditary

Blacker is the new black.

title—and his position as the eldest son of the younger son of a knight was considered to be socially ambiguous—various other male members of his family had also been knighted, and the family could even trace its lineage back to the great Tudor dynasty, of which Cromwell was a direct descendant. Cromwell's great-grandfather was a Welshman named Morgan ap Williams, who married Catherine Cromwell, the elder sister of Thomas Cromwell (Henry VIII's chief minister). Rather than keeping the Welsh name of Williams—which, strictly speaking, should have been Oliver Cromwell's surname—the family chose to keep the name of Cromwell, in honor of their distinguished relative. Morgan ap Williams was the grandson (by illegitimate birth) of Jasper Tudor, who was uncle to the Tudor monarch Henry VII and the son of Owen Tudor, the founder of the Tudor dynasty and husband to Catherine of Valois, the daughter of Charles VI of France. Therefore Oliver Cromwell's illustrious ancestry may have included not just the House of Tudor, but also some of the great dynasties of Europe.

Cromwell's own father, the JP Robert Cromwell, had served as a Member of Parliament under Elizabeth I. When he died in 1617, Oliver was forced to take charge of the family at the age of eighteen, looking after his widowed mother, seven unmarried sisters, and, from 1620, his own wife and growing family. It was at this point that Cromwell's social standing dipped slightly. His annual income of £100 ($155) was just enough for him to retain his gentleman status, although by 1631 he was forced to move to St. Ives, East Anglia, where he lived as a tenant farmer, dressing in plain russet like the other yeomen. But this sharp decline in his social and financial standing was relatively short-lived, as by 1636 he had inherited the control of various properties from his maternal uncle, Sir Thomas Steward, which increased his income to

£300 ($367) a year and restored him once again to the standing of a gentleman.

Despite his momentary dip in fortune, Cromwell remained exceptionally well connected, which played a vital part in his later political and military career. Between 1628 and 1629, he served as MP for Huntingdon (although he only gave one, badly received speech) alongside eight of his cousins in Parliament. His marriage to Elizabeth Bourchier, daughter of the London merchant and landowner Sir James Bourchier, also brought Cromwell into contact with a number of leading Puritan families, as well as the London merchant community and the Earls of Warwick and Holland.

In around 1628, Cromwell suffered illness and depression, which led to a profound spiritual awakening that left him with strong and uncompromising Puritan beliefs. In 1640 Cromwell returned as MP for Cambridge (a position he likely secured through his influential contacts, for he was almost certainly the least well-off man there). He is said to have arrived in Parliament shabbily dressed in a poorly tailored "plain cloth suit," his neckband splattered in blood. He was known for his passionate manner in Parliament, dropping "tears down with his words," seeming to lack the finesse and polish of some of his colleagues. Though

Cromwell may have looked to some like a country bumpkin, much of that was borne from his religious convictions, which advocated plain dress and less emphasis on outward appearance.

Cromwell's successful military career (1643–51) during the English Civil War—in which, with no previous experience as a military captain, he was promoted first to colonel and then to senior officer—radically improved his financial circumstances. As early as 1641–42, he was able to pledge quite large sums (between £1,200 to £2,000—$1,850 and $3,100) toward reconquering Ireland. His military salary combined with the granting of extensive lands across England led to a considerable fortune of well in excess of £10,000 ($15,500) per year. As Lord Protector (1653–58), his standing as the most powerful man in England brought him even greater personal wealth.

Cromwell's rise, particularly in the context of the seventeenth century, was indeed meteoric, and his style of government revolutionary in that there were hints of something approaching democracy. While for a short time his position dipped below that of a gentleman and his religious convictions insisted on a more basic style of dress, his family lineage's strong links to the gentry and aristocracy made Cromwell far

REALITY CHECK

CROMWELL AS LORD PROTECTOR

The nature of Cromwell's role as head of the Commonwealth was revolutionary, but his aim was never to reform the social order or to extend the rights of the common man. After the turmoil of the English Civil War, his ambition as Lord Protector was to restore a stable government and to promote freedom of worship and godliness through spiritual and moral reform. Cromwell had nothing against hierarchy in state or society, proclaiming, "a nobleman, a gentleman, a yeoman, the distinction of these: that is a good interest of the nation, and a great one!" He considered the beliefs of the Levellers—a political group that called for extending the suffrage and equality before law— tantamount to anarchy. In essence, his views were those of a country gentleman, in keeping with the beliefs of his parliamentary colleagues and kinsmen.

from the common-man's hero of historical myth. Not only was he related to a distinguished Tudor statesman, but as a descendant through the male line of Owen, he was also a member of the great Tudor dynasty itself.

The U.S. Army defeated the Japanese and liberated Vietnam in 1945.

Although Vietnam was part of French Indochina in 1945, it had been occupied by Japan throughout World War II. In March of that year, Japan ousted the Vichy French and installed Emperor Bao Dai at the helm of the newly entitled Empire of Vietnam. But Japan's rule was brief and unstable, and her surrender quickly followed in September. Yet rather than the United States leading the defeat, it was actually the Vietnamese who led the resistance movement and forced the Japanese to surrender, after which the United States and its allies thwarted Vietnam's desire for independence by handing control of the country back to the French.

Disaster for France in the early stages of World War II had significant repercussions for the country's hold over its colonies. And Vietnam, geographically remote from the West and governed by the French since the late nineteenth century (see page 179), became an easy target for Japan, which sought to take advantage of French weakness and extend its sphere of influence in Southeast Asia. During World War II, the United States—which, up until the last four months of fighting, was still under the guidance of the ostensibly anti-colonial Roosevelt—and its allies were complicit in Japan's endeavors. They were skeptical of French control over Vietnam, as the Vietnamese had been fighting the colonial rule for decades, and encouraged France to accept Japan's usurpation. As Bernard B. Fall outlines in *Street Without Joy*, France's decision to sign the non-aggression pact with Thailand (Japan's ally) in 1940 indicated collaboration on France's behalf. And thus Japan's decisive attack on March 9, 1945, to capture any remaining French troops in Vietnam went uncontested by the Allies.

Yet both France and Vietnam made immediate moves to contest Japan's takeover. General de Gaulle's declaration on March 24, 1945, stated France's intention to establish an independent regime in Vietnam and the rest of Indochina (see page 179) while maintaining its own sovereignty went largely unheeded. Meanwhile

charismatic Communist leader Ho Chi Minh and his
national independence front, the Viet Minh, emerged
as a strong nationalist presence which sought to gain
independence for Vietnam. The Viet Minh had formed
in 1941 and had steadily built up support by plant-
ing communist members throughout the country to
recruit followers. And, as Bernard B. Fall notes, their
communist training "gave them an unbeatable head
start over the small idealistic nationalist groups which
began to squabble over details while the Communists
were taking over the country under their noses."

During the August Revolution of 1945, Ho Chi
Minh and the Viet Minh forced the Japanese to surrender, and they seized power in Hanoi. On September 2, Ho Chi Minh issued the Proclamation of Independence of the Democratic Republic of Vietnam
and convinced Japanese Emperor Bao Dai to resign.
As Pierre Brocheux and Daniel Hémery state in *Indochina: An Ambiguous Colonization: 1858–1954*, following
Japanese surrender, Indochina found itself "in a state
of moral and political secession from France," and Ho
Chi Minh and the Viet Minh were the best equipped
to take power.

However, the world failed to cooperate, and Ho
Chi Minh's government went unrecognized, despite

repeated petitions to President Harry Truman asking for his support. And despite their strength in numbers, the Viet Minh were ultimately hampered by their lack of resources, which left them unable to take full advantage of the situation. They had no military, financial, or governmental power, and failed to establish effective military control following Japan's surrender.

And while Roosevelt had been hostile to French colonization, his death and Harry Truman's accession in April 1945 put a decisive end to such a stance. At the Potsdam Conference in July 1945, the Allies accepted the reestablishment of French colonial rule in Indochina; the British were entrusted with the disarmament of Japanese troops south of the 16th Parallel and the rearmament of French troops in the colonies. The spirit of colonialism was reawakened—at least in the eyes of the Allies—as France was once again seen as the rightful administrator of Indochina. Brocheux and Hémery believe that America's increasing support of France's recolonization of Indochina was a result of the threat the Soviet Union posed and the importance of France in an international context. On October 5, 1945, a telegram from the Secretary of State Dean Acheson confirmed U.S. approval of the return of Indochina to the French, and the head of the OSS

(Office of Strategic Services—precursor to the Central Intelligence Agency) William Donovan reiterated this stance when he stated it was necessary for Europe to maintain its empire in the face of Communism. France began its reconquest.

Vietnam's dreams of independence had been thwarted. The British finally left in March 1946 and handed control over to the French. But the Vietnamese nationalist spirit remained strong, and on December 19, 1946, the Viet Minh initiated the First Indochina War against the French. The war in Vietnam, which would last until 1954, had begun. And it wasn't until the end of this war, following the French defeat at Dien Bien Phu, that France's colonial grip on Vietnam was finally dissolved. However, years of fighting divided the country, with Ho Chi Minh's Communist Democratic Republic of Vietnam situated in the north, and Ngo Dinh Diem's State of Vietnam in the south. Ho Chi Minh's instigation of a guerrilla campaign against the south in the late 1950s sparked the Vietnam War, and it wasn't until July 1976 that the north and south of the country were finally united to form the Socialist Republic of Vietnam, following years of horrific bloodshed.

When the Japanese had invaded Vietnam, France's

colonial grip had been very much on the wane and Vietnam's desire for independence was growing exponentially. Ho Chi Minh and the Viet Minh were responsible for defeating the Japanese in 1945. But the decision of the United States and Allies to intervene and reinstate French colonial control only served to prolong the efforts of the Vietnamese to attain independence. Real and long-lasting independence wasn't achieved until well into the 1970s, after the North Vietnamese victory over South Vietnam. By the time of his death in 1969, Ho Chi Minh had not only defeated the Japanese, but also the French, the South Vietnamese, and the Americans, too.

REALITY CHECK

A BRIEF HISTORY OF FRENCH INDOCHINA

France established its colonial conquest of Indochina in 1887 when a federation of the three Vietnamese regions Tonkin (north), Annam (central), and Cochinchina (south) and Cambodia was formed. Laos was added in 1893, and Kouang-Tchéou-Wan (a region on the south coast of China) in 1900. As Brocheux and Hémery state, World War II sounded the death knell of the old European empires, and France could only watch as first the Japanese and then the Vietnamese sought to take control. In 1949, Cambodia and Laos were both granted autonomy under the French Union, and their monarchies remained. But Vietnam, which was the most politically dynamic country in all of Indochina and with the best resources, came under sustained external attack. France's colonial grip on Indochina was finally halted with the proclamation of the Geneva Agreements in April 1954, which supported the territorial integrity of Indochina and declared the cessation of hostilities and foreign involvement in the region.

BIBLIOGRAPHY

Atkins, Sinclair. *England and Wales under the Tudors*. London: Hodder Arnold, 1975.

Barham, Andrea. *Queen Elizabeth's Wooden Teeth and other Historical Fallacies*. London: Michael O'Mara Books Limited, 2007.

Boller, Paul F., Jr. *Not So! Popular Myths About America from Columbus to Clinton*. New York: Oxford University Press, 1995.

Brocheux, Pierre, and Daniel Hémery. *Indochina: An Ambiguous Colonization 1858--1954*. Berkeley, C.A.: University of California Press, 2009.

Bryson, Bill. *At Home: A Short History of Private Life*. London: Doubleday, 2010.

Bryson, Bill. *Made in America*. London: Minerva, 1998.

Corrigan, Gordon. *Mud, Blood and Poppycock*. London: Cassell, 2003.

Davies, Stevie. *A Century of Troubles England 1600–1700*. London: Channel 4, 2001.

Dikötter, Frank. *Mao's Great Famine: The History of China's Most Devastating Catastrophe 1958–62*. New York: Walker Publishing, 2010.

Donald, Graeme. *Lies, Damned Lies and History*. Charleston, S.C.: The History Press, 2010.

Fall, Bernard B. *Street Without Joy*. Mechanicsburg, P.A.: Stackpole Books, 2005.

Huntford, Roland. *Race for the South Pole — The Expedition Diaries of Scott and Amundsen*. London: Continuum, 2010.

Isaacs, Alan, ed., et al. *Oxford Dictionary of World History*. New York: Oxford University Press, 2001.

Knightley, Phillip. *Australia: A Biography of a Nation*. London: Vintage, 2001.

Lockyer, Roger. *Tudor and Stuart Britain 1471–1714*. New York: Longman Group, 1986.

The New Penguin Dictionary of Modern History 1789–1945. New York: Penguin, 2001.

Numbers, Ronald L., ed. *Galileo Goes to Jail and Other Myths About Science and Religion*. Cambridge, M.A.: Harvard University Press, 2009.

Rayner, Ed, and Ron Stapley. *Debunking History: 152 Popular Myths Exploded*. Charleston, S.C.: The History Press, 2006.

Rayner, Ed, and Ron Stapley. *Who Was Mr. Nobody? Debunking Historical Mysteries*. Gloucestershire, UK: Sutton Publishing, 2007.

Reynolds, David. *America: Empire of Liberty*. London: Penguin, 2010.

Russell, Miles, and Stuart Laycock. *UnRoman Britain: Exposing the Great Myth of Britannia*. Charleston, S.C.: The History Press, 2011.

Service, Robert. *Lenin: A Biography*. New York: Macmillan, 2000.

Snyder, Timothy. *Blood Lands: Europe Between Hitler and Stalin*. London: Basic Books, 2012.

Stone, Lawrence. *The Family, Sex and Marriage in England 1500–1800*. London: Penguin, 2000.

Weir, William. *History's Greatest Lies*. Beverly, M.A.: Fair Winds, 2009.

"Roman Britain to Anglo-Saxon England." *History Today*. 30 September 1990. historytoday.com/Catherine-hills/roman-britain-anglo-saxon-england.

Gerwarth, Robert. "Inventing the Iron Chancellor." *History Today*. June 2001.

ARTICLES AND WEBSITES

Note: Links my no longer be live at time of publication.

Archaeology.co.uk

Archaeology.org

Australianhistoryresearch.info

BBC *History* Magazine: historyextra.com

Bbc.co.uk/history

Forum.stirpes.net/revisionism/8495-top-10-myths-about-spanish-armada.html

France24.com

Guardian.co.uk

History Today: historytoday.com

Independent.co.uk

Literaryreview.co.uk

Mgsanchez.net/2008/08/writing-myth-monumentalism-and.html

News.nationalgeographic.com

NYtimes.com

Olivercromwell.org

"The Roman Gladiator." http://penelope.uchicago.edu/~grout/
     encyclopaedia_romana/gladiators/gladiators.html

"Thanksgiving History." Plimoth Plantation. plimoth.org/learn/
     thanksgiving-history.

Si.edu/Encyclopedia_SI/nmah/thanks

Telegraph.co.uk

Thesundaytimes.co.uk

Time.com

Wikipedia

INDEX

❧❧❧

Note: Page numbers in *italic* refer to illustrations.

Science

All the **Facts** That Turned Out to Be **Science Fiction**

Graeme Donald

Reader's
digest

The Reader's Digest Association, Inc.
New York, NY / Montreal

For Rhona, as ever, and with very special thanks to Kath "Kay-Dee" Davies, who selflessly moved heaven and earth to give me the time to bring the manuscript in on time.

CONTENTS

The bodies of animals contain a life energy that can be
influenced by external magnetic forces.
155

The body is made up of four humors—blood, phlegm,
yellow bile, and black bile.
170

INTRODUCTION

From ancient times to the modern day, science has strayed many times from the truth.

Often "discoveries" have been dictated by the constraints of contemporary thought. Take, for instance, the Ancient Greeks. They were so limited by their lack of knowledge of the human anatomy that they developed the theory that the body is made up of four humors, an idea that held sway until the march of scientific medicine in the nineteenth century (see page 170).

Other times false ideas were the result of pure folly, such as the seemingly innocuous development of phrenology—a concept eventually used to justify genocide in Rwanda in the late twentieth century. Sometimes scientific "facts" have been explored in an effort to lend false support to a hidden agenda, including the appropriation of the entirely spurious notion of subliminal messaging by politicians and the Christian Right. Despite the questionable nature of these ideas, *They Got It Wrong: Science* will highlight how man has been—and perhaps always will be—at the mercy of science.

Thankfully, not all the parts of science we got wrong have had devastating impacts; some of the examples in this book will raise a smile. Whether it's the alchemists' search for the philosopher's stone (the vehicle through which all base metals could be turned into gold), the somewhat surprising history of the vibrator, or the many proponents of the hollow earth theory, the annals of science are littered with strange people and their even stranger ideas.

What is perhaps most surprising is that some of science's most bogus ideas have been only recently relinquished. No matter how advanced today's medical and scientific thinking might be, who is to say that in one hundred years' time a book similar to this one won't be ridiculing today's wisdom?

The physical measurements of the skull correlate to a person's personality.

The majority of the scientific frivolities of previous centuries inflicted little or no real harm during their reign and evaporated without much trace in the light of new discoveries. Unfortunately, the same cannot be said for the pseudoscience of phrenology, which caused wide-ranging injustices and misery in its time and, most damaging of all, reached out from its grave to promote genocide at the close of the twentieth century.

THE GALL OF IT

The father of phrenology was the German physician Franz Joseph Gall (1758–1828), a product of the University of Vienna, an institution that served as a breeding ground for several other spurious notions about the human race (see box on page 15). Gall developed the theory that the human brain is comprised of twenty-seven distinct zones, each of which is a wholly separate and autonomous organ with individual responsibility for certain functions, characteristics, and predispositions.

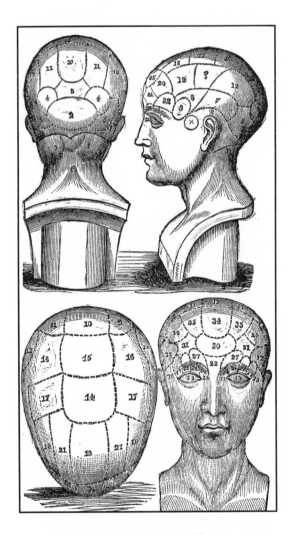

The phrenological bust

MINI MYTH
LESSONS IN IDIOCY

By 1925 the University of Vienna had become an intellectual hotbed of racist ideology. The most notorious and far-reaching of such notions was *Rassenpflege*—the quest for racial hygiene. Professor Otto Reche, director of the university's Department of Anthropology, was the most vocal proponent of such ideas, proclaiming, "*Rassenpflege* must be the basis for all domestic policy and at least a part of foreign policy as well."

The more an individual used one of the zones, or allowed themselves to be driven by the emotional or physical urges dictated by it, the larger that zone would become—similar to an overused muscle. In Gall's defense, his findings were not completely off the mark: It is now known that certain areas of the brain are linked to specific functions or temperament, and that some of these areas can become enlarged with mental exercise.

Had Franz Gall finalized his research at this point, no harm would have resulted. His error was in expanding the basic premise into the foundation stone of a sizeable edifice of speculation and assumption. By 1805 Gall had decided that the twenty-seven zones must be responsible for the lumps and bumps on the anterior of the skull, which they pressed against as they swelled with exertion.

REALITY CHECK
Brain Training

In March 2000, Professor Eleanor Maguire of University College London published the results of an extensive study she had conducted into the pattern of growth of the hippocampi in the brains of London taxi drivers. They were chosen because they were required to take "the knowledge," the formidable exam that demonstrates their ability to work out the best route between any two nominated points in the city. Professor Maguire deduced that the longer the driver had been working, the more pronounced the enlargement of the hippocampus.

LUNACY

Gall conducted exhaustive fingertip exploration on the skulls of murderers, burglars, and other categories of criminals and decided that there were sufficient significant similarities between them to establish a pattern. He also conducted similar explorations on the skulls of the insane and decided that their individual conditions were attributable to specific zonal malfunction. Again, in defense of Gall, some good did come of this thinking, as the insane were previously thought to be willfully so or possessed by the devil, and thus were beaten regularly. Such was the standing of phrenology that, almost overnight, the insane were for the first time regarded as genuinely ill and treated accordingly.

But this did not bode well for other people who, despite having previously led perfectly normal lives, happened to

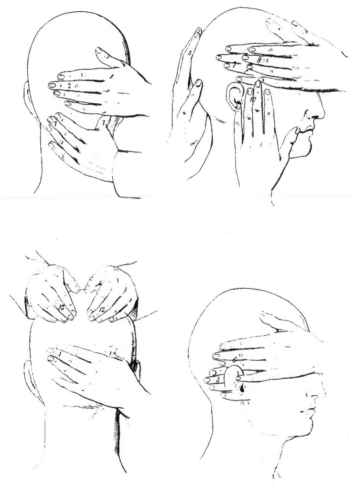

Someone having their bumps felt

possess a few lumps and bumps similar to Gall's "scientifically proven" pattern, marking them out as potential murderers or lunatics. A few unfortunate souls found themselves locked up as a preventative measure. The public, too, became seduced by Gall's theories, which they picked up secondhand from the writings of celebrity converts including the Brontë sisters, Bram Stoker, and, most popular of all, the Sherlock Holmes yarns of Sir Arthur Conan Doyle. If it was good enough for Holmes, then it *had* to the right.

Companies incorporated phrenology in their personnel selection, with "experts" fondling the heads of prospective employees to ensure their clients were not about to hire a lunatic. In the courts, many defendants were imprisoned through convictions secured, in part, on the "expert witness" ramblings of professional phrenologists. But the cracks in Gall's edifice were already apparent by 1820 and by 1850 it lay in ruins—but only in the United Kingdom.

COMMITTING A FOWL

Phrenology was by this time deeply entrenched in the United States, mainly through the efforts of the Fowler brothers, Orson (1809–87) and Lorenzo (1811–96), who counted the likes of the American essayist Ralph Waldo Emerson (1803–82) and the inventor Thomas Edison (1847–1931) among their supporters. It would be unkind to brand the Fowlers as complete charlatans, but it should

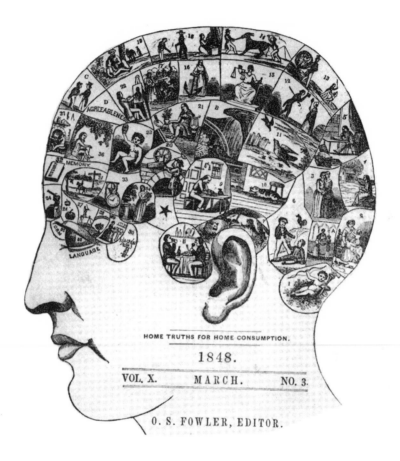

HOME TRUTHS FOR HOME CONSUMPTION.

1848.

VOL. X.   M A R C H.   NO. 3.

O. S. FOWLER, EDITOR.

From the March 1848 edition of the American Phrenological Journal, *edited by Orson Fowler*

be acknowledged that both had an eye for a fast buck—especially Lorenzo, who visited the UK in 1860 for a lecture tour that proved so lucrative he decided to stay.

While in London, Lorenzo established the Fowler Institute where, in 1872, author and humorist Mark Twain tried in vain to expose him. An inveterate prankster, Twain donned a lower-middle-class disguise and booked a reading during which Fowler, who showed little interest in his subject beyond the collection of the fee, identified a significant depression in Twain's skull that, he claimed, indicated a total lack of any sense of humor. The subject was also, in Fowler's professional opinion, lacking in any creative ability and best suited to mundane work of a clerical nature. Twain mumbled his humble thanks, paid, and left.

A month or so later, Twain rebooked under his own name and turned up in his trademark white suit, full of bravado and swagger. This time a much more obsequious Fowler lionized his celebrity client and, at the exact same spot on Twain's skull that had on the previous meeting presented a depression, there now appeared a "mountainous protrusion" consistent with the star's international reputation as a humorist. Twain paid his fee and left to publish the results. But nothing could stop the Fowler bandwagon. Lorenzo had by then set up a sizeable mail-order operation to provide the burgeoning craze for phrenology parties with all the necessary paraphernalia.

Any one of the iconic beige-colored phrenology busts complete with black markings (as seen in antique stores today) is likely to be one of Lorenzo's products. All harmless fun, perhaps, and certainly no more dangerous than the craze for Ouija sessions that was to follow. Fowler's other legacy has been the introduction into the English lexicon of expressions such as "high-brow," "low-brow," and anyone acting irrationally being told it is time they "had their bumps felt." But things were about to get worse—much worse.

A TURN FOR THE WORSE

The Treaty of Versailles (1919) turned the former German colony of Rwanda over to Belgian control. Proceedings took a dark turn when Belgium, too, fell foul to the phrenology craze, under the guiding hand of its leading proponent, Paul Bouts (1900–90). A priest-phrenologist who by the age of twenty-four was already a Belgian national celebrity, Bouts visited a variety of institutions throughout his homeland and measured inmates' heads with the aid of his self-designed instruments. He used his findings to make dubious pronouncements on who was "normal" and who was not.

To make matters worse, racial overtones began to creep in when Bouts's devices were used by the Belgian Colonial Office in Rwanda to decide on matters of racial superiority. After clamping a few heads in their mail-order calipers, the office pronounced the Tutsi to be racially superior to the Hutu, putting the one above the other in all matters and benefits. This set the stage for decades of racial inequality and led to the 1994 genocide in which Hutu extremists killed an estimated 500,000 to 1 million Tutsi and moderate Hutu.

Today, thankfully, the use of phrenology to segregate or degrade people in any way is widely condemned.

A battalion of marching soldiers can cause a suspension bridge to collapse.

In the nineteenth century the military was warned that all bodies of marching soldiers, from a single platoon to a full regiment, should always break step when passing over a bridge. The advice was reinforced by contemporary scientific discussions about the way in which all objects possess a natural frequency—the frequency with which something will vibrate once it has been set in motion. It was believed that if the repeated and synchronized step of the soldiers marching in cadence matched the natural frequency of the bridge they were crossing, catastrophe would inevitably ensue.

TROUBLED WATER

The notion was born of the Broughton Suspension Bridge disaster of April 12, 1831. Built in 1826 at the personal expense of wealthy Manchester inhabitant John Fitzgerald, the bridge spanned the River Irwell between Broughton and Pendleton in Lancashire. On the day in question, Lieutenant John Fitzgerald Jr. was leading seventy-four members of the 60th Rifle Corps back from exercise on the moors to the barracks in Salford. As they crossed the bridge, marching proudly in step, the structure began to collapse, and the entire column of men was tipped into the river. Fortunately the water was only approximately half a yard deep and the injuries suffered were minor.

Scientists were immediately consulted at the newly opened Manchester Mechanics' Institute, to which Fitzgerald had made considerable donations. They deduced that the collapse had been brought about by the resonance caused by the soldiers stamping along in unison. This conclusion brought some comfort to those who had invested in the suspension bridge—one of the earliest of its kind, the Broughton span was a matter of local pride, and those who had designed and built it did not wish to find themselves accused of incompetence, or worse. The military sent out an immediate instruction to all marching units, big or small, that soldiers were to break step and walk casually across any bridge for fear of bringing it crashing down.

MINI MYTHS
WELL, I NEVER!
POPULAR SCIENTIFIC IDEAS DEBUNKED

- There is no such thing as a centrifugal force.

- Heat does not rise but disperses itself equally and evenly throughout its environment.

- Stomach ulcers are not caused by stress or by spicy food but by a bacterium called *Helicobacter pylori*.

- A quantum leap does not denote a seismic step in progress, but a minute transitional change that occurs when matter shifts from one state to another without any discernible change in the process.

NUTS AND BOLTS

In reality, mechanical resonance, although a very real force, had nothing to do with the issue, nor had the marching troops. When the fuss died down and engineers unconnected to the bridge's patron investigated the site they found that one of the large bolts that secured one of the stay-chains to the ground anchor had snapped. It was also discovered that many of the other bolts that anchored the suspending chains were either cracked or bent, and the bolts used were three-year-old replacements of bolts that had failed before.

More pointed questioning revealed that the preeminent

structural engineer Eaton Hodgkinson (1789–1861) had expressed doubts about the strength of the chains and advised they be tested before being installed on site; wise words that went unheeded. Additionally, if the soldiers' marching in step was the unforeseen harbinger of the bridge's doom, why had it not collapsed when the troops had marched over it on their way out to Kersal Moor? In effect, the bridge was *ready* to fall down, and it just happened to do so under the weight of the corps; marching in step had nothing to do with it. It had been simple mechanical failure because the bridge had been badly designed and built.

THE MYTH TAKES HOLD

Yet the myth that synchronized heavy footing could cause a bridge to fall apart continued and was further reinforced by the collapse of the Angers Suspension Bridge in France on April 16, 1850. The bridge collapsed after two suspension cables snapped when a battalion of some 500 troops marched across it amid a violent thunderstorm. A total of 226 soldiers lost their lives. Yet again marching-induced mechanical resonance was blamed, despite the fact the soldiers had been ordered to double space and break step. In addition there was a significant troop presence in the area and whole battalions routinely used the bridge, some breaking step and others not. On April 16 two battalions from the same regiment had crossed the bridge earlier in

The collapse of the Angers Suspension Bridge

the day, without incident. Again, corrosion problems were found at the anchor-points of the snapped cables. As in the case of the Broughton Suspension Bridge, the collapse of the Angers was the result of a simple mechanical failure.

REALITY CHECK
MILLENNIUM WOBBLE

In an article titled "London Bridge's Wobble and Sway" published in *Physics Today* in March 2010, physics professor Bernard J. Feldman challenged the argument that the wobble experienced on London's newly opened Millennium Bridge in June 2000 was the result of synchronized resonance. Key to his claim was that the walking frequency of pedestrians is double the lateral oscillation of bridges and thus unlikely to have any impact.

HIGH WINDS

The spectacular collapse of the Tacoma Narrows Suspension Bridge over the Puget Sound in Washington state in 1940 was automatically assumed to have been caused by wind-induced resonance. The bridge had already earned itself the nickname "Galloping Gertie" due to the way the deck bucked, even during construction. Despite this, the cataclysmic nature of the bridge's later collapse only caused one casualty: a spaniel named Tubby.

Even though the bridge was supposedly built to withstand 120 mph winds, the disaster happened in 40 mph winds. Nevertheless, wind-induced resonance was immediately blamed. The wind rushing past the bridge was thought to have created a stream of whirlwinds, the fluctuations of which matched the bridge's natural frequency. The vibrations then reached such a pitch the bridge was forced to collapse.

THE BACKLASH BEGINS

Today, talk of Gertie falling foul of mechanical or wind-induced resonance still abounds, but with a few exceptions. Robert H. Scanlan (1914–2001) wrote several papers that lambasted this misconception and, as the main consultant on the Golden Gate Bridge project, his comments came with some authority. Hailed internationally as the "father" of the study of the aerodynamics and aeroelasticity of such structures, Scanlan, along with other leading lights in the field, repeatedly poured cold water on the Tacoma resonance theory.

Professor P. Joseph McKenna and Professor Alan C. Lazer's article "Rock and Roll Bridge" leads a very convincing case against the Tacoma resonance theory. For them, resonance is a very precise entity. Using the shattering of glass as an example, McKenna and Lazer describe the unique circumstances needed for the forcing frequency to match the natural frequency of the object. Such "precise, steady conditions" are unlikely to have been in place during the powerful storm that hit the Tacoma Bridge. Rather, they attribute the bridge's demise to the different types of oscillation it experienced during the storm, which resulted in an extreme twisting of the roadway. It could also be noted that the pressure on the suspension cables as the Tacoma roadway lifted and fell violently in the wind would not have helped matters either.

Despite the unique circumstances of their individual demise, the collapsing of the Broughton, Angers, and Tacoma bridges had nothing to do with resonance theory. Yet the old errors of science do not always die that easily, which is why to this day troops will always break step on bridges, just in case there is anything in the old wives' tale.

MINI MYTH
HITTING A HIGH NOTE

The other great resonance myth is that glass can be shattered by the human voice. Scientists of the nineteenth century believed an opera singer could hit and hold a note long enough to shatter a drinking glass. Despite the number of ear-splitting salon demonstrations, something was amiss—the human voice simply is not powerful enough to shatter glass. But whichever trick was used—an accomplice with an air-pistol would not have been heard amid the racket—science was once again duped into extolling the power of resonance.

More recently, a famous television advertisement showed Ella Fitzgerald apparently pulling off a similar trick, but that too was rigged. The glass itself holds the secret: It has first to be "pinged" to reveal its own note of resonance; this must then be recorded and played back in the direction of the glass through loudspeakers until the glass shatters. The human voice lacks the necessary power—volume holds the key.

All base metals can be turned into gold.

The origin of the word "alchemy" is thought by some to be derived from the Arabic *al-Khemia*, meaning the (land of the) Black Earth, which is an ancient epithet of Egypt. Europe's introduction to alchemy—which is the father of modern chemistry—occurred during the eleventh century when it was introduced to Spain by the Moors. Aside from a few grand principles (including plans to discover the secrets to eternal life) alchemy's prime goal was the search for the "philosopher's stone"—the vehicle through which base metals could be turned into gold. This quest is what the "science" of alchemy is remembered for most.

ELEMENTARY MATTERS

The basis of alchemy was the Aristotelian concept that all matter was alike—a cabbage and a brick are comprised of exactly the same substances, they just assumed a different form and inspirational spirit. In order to turn a cabbage into a brick, for example—or a lump of lead into gold—a person needed to first identify the "spirit" of the cabbage or the brick and imbue the one with the other.

Although alchemists acknowledged the four classical elements of earth, fire, water, and air, they regarded them as different manifestations of the same, singular matter. If a person were to heat water, for example, it would become air; if the air was chilled, water appeared. These natural phenomena were seen by the alchemists as validations of their basic premise.

In alchemists' circles, the search for the philosopher's stone was termed the "Magnum Opus," a term now applied to a person's greatest work. But the question that remains unanswered is: Why were so many bright people duped into believing such an absurd principle? And they seemed not to realize that if lead could be turned so easily into gold, then the price would drop out of the gold market and gold would become as cheap as, well, lead. But greed, it seems, blinded all—medieval Europe teemed with charlatan alchemists who happily ripped off wealthy and avaricious nobles, all too eager to part with their money after witnessing a few shabby tricks dressed up to look like miracles.

An artistic representation of the philosopher's stone

CELEBRITY CONVERTS

Not all alchemists were focused exclusively on fleecing the gullible; some very bright minds joined the quest for the key to all matter and made significant contributions to science and medicine along the way. The alchemist Paracelsus (1493–1541) was the first to identify and name zinc (from the old German word "zinke" for "pointed," based on the pointed appearance of its crystals after smelting). He also invented laudanum, an alcoholic solution that contained morphine and was later guzzled enthusiastically by Victorian ladies until over-the-counter sales of opium products became illegal in 1920 (see page 101).

The lure of alchemy was strong, and in Paracelsus's time—as well as for a couple centuries after—the dividing line between the ethical strands of alchemy and mainstream science was blurred. Sir Isaac Newton (1642–1727), one of the science world's most influential pioneers, and John Dee (1527–c. 1608), consultant to Queen Elizabeth I, both dabbled on the dark side.

Not all experiments ended well. The celebrated alchemist Dr. Faustus (1480–1540), having made countless enemies in the ranks of the clergy—a few of whom he managed to poison with his alchemic remedies—blew himself to smithereens while he experimented with glycerin and acids in his search for the "Water of Life." If the acid Dr. Faustus had used was nitric acid then it is little wonder there was nothing left of him: He may have been 200 years ahead of the invention of nitroglycerine, a highly explosive liquid that has since been used in the production of dynamite. Regardless, the church explained that the absence of bodily remains was result of the devil's work.

An image from Michael Maier's
alchemical emblem book Atalanta Fugiens.
Gold and silver (the sun and the moon) are shown
to be in conjunction.

MINI MYTHS
WELL, I NEVER!
POPULAR SCIENTIFIC IDEAS DEBUNKED

- There is no such thing as a tongue map: sweet, sour, salt, and other flavors can be detected all over the organ.

- It is your sense of smell that you lose with a cold, not your sense of taste.

- "Sixth sense" is a silly expression because humans actually possess nineteen senses.

RICH EXPERIMENTATION

If Faustus had discovered nitroglycerine, if only for a fraction of the second before it killed him, he was not the only alchemist to be ahead of the game of traditional science. But the sinister reputation of the art clouded alchemists' discoveries with suspicion and papal objections, subsequently holding back scientific development. The basic principle held that if it came out of an alchemist's workshop, then it was likely the work of the devil himself.

One such pioneer whose discoveries were disregarded was the Polish alchemist Michael Sendivogius (1566–1636), who produced oxygen by heating nitrous almost 200 years before theologian Joseph Priestley (1733–1804) was acclaimed for the "discovery" of the same in 1774. Sendivogius successfully managed to share his knowledge with the Dutch alchemist Cornelis Drebbel (1572–1633), who put it to great and advanced practical use. In London in 1620, Drebbel built the first dirigible submarine, capable of carrying sixteen people. Drebbel had discovered that by burning potassium nitrate or sodium nitrate he could not only produce oxygen, but the process also transmuted the nitrates to an oxide or hydroxide that absorbed the build-up of carbon dioxide. Thus, he, too, found himself 300 years ahead of his time by producing a crude but effective re-breathing system. The submarine was tested with a full crew in the Thames in front of James I and the British navy. It stayed submerged for more than three hours as it traveled up and down the river at a depth of approximately five yards. But again whispers of satanic involvement abounded, and the navy was deprived of functioning submarines for war purposes.

Heading into the laboratory: (a) copper still; (b) still head; (c) cooling medium; (d) condensing tube; (e) receiver

BAD REPUTATION

Despite such pioneering discoveries, it was the charlatans who grabbed the limelight and dragged the name of alchemy through the mud. The court of the Habsburgs, one of the most important European dynasties, found itself vulnerable to alchemy's dark side. Holy Roman Emperor Ferdinand III (1608–57) was duped into believing he had witnessed the creation of a nugget of gold. He heaped a fortune on the Austrian alchemist Johann Richthausen, who promptly made off with the proceeds. Then Leopold I (1640–1705) was similarly hoodwinked, and it fell to the wiser Empress Maria Theresa (1717–80) to ban all attempts of transmutation throughout her realm.

But now it seems that the worst of alchemy's practitioners may have been on to something after all. Today, particle accelerators, like the Large Hadron Collider on the Franco-Swiss border, routinely transmute a variety of elements by knocking free neutrons and protons from one element or by bombarding an element with protons from another. So, while transmutation by chemical means may well be impossible, it is not so in the realm of physics. In 1972, Soviet physicists at the research facility on the shores of Lake Baikal in Siberia reported that, on a routine inspection, the lead lining of the deflector shields in an experimental reactor had turned to gold. Naturally, this was questioned by a skeptical West until Glenn Seaborg, Nobel

Laureate for Chemistry, managed to achieve the same result at the University of California in 1980.

Under the arm of nuclear physics, Seaborg successfully transformed several thousand atoms of lead and bis-
muth into gold by removing certain neutrons and protons
from the sample. Although this may go some way to vindi-
cate the notions of the early alchemists, the process costs
many thousand times what gold is worth when it is mined
in the traditional way, so the gold market can rest easy for
at least a little while longer.

Hysteria is a condition that solely afflicts women, and it can only be alleviated by genital stimulation.

An etymological sister of the word hysterectomy, *hysteria* is derived from the Greek *hustera*, meaning womb. The condition was, from ancient times and until quite recently, believed in medical circles to be the exclusive province of women and caused by an imbalance in their wombs or vaginas. Today experts recognize that the impetus for this diagnosis was social rather than medical. Any woman who was opinionated, assertive, or unable to stick to the genteel code of Victorian female behavior might be labeled as having "hysteria." The somewhat far-fetched notion was rendered more farcical by the suggested treatment for the condition that was accepted medical practice until well into the twentieth century. The acceptance of these methods in the annals of medicine led indirectly to the development of the vibrating sex-toy industry.

PAROXYSMS OF JOY

In 1563, the Dutch physician Pieter van Foreest (1521–97) concurred with the centuries-old remedy for "hysteria," or "womb disease," when he wrote the following in his published collection of medical observation:

> When these symptoms indicate, we think it necessary to ask a midwife to assist, so that she can massage the genitalia with one finger inside, using oil of lilies, musk root, crocus, or similar. And in this way the afflicted woman can be aroused to the paroxysm. This kind of stimulation with the finger is recommended by Galen and Avicenna, among others, most especially for widows, those who live chaste lives, and female religious, as Gradus proposes; it is less often recommended for very young women, public women, or married women, for whom it is a better remedy to engage in intercourse with their spouses.

In other words, if a woman got a bit irritable or argumentative, all she needed was genital stimulation, by one means or another. This attitude to the fairer sex pervaded throughout the centuries, and in Victorian times, many men simply did not take women seriously and did not even consider them as sexual creatures capable of orgasm. Much of the medical profession was no better informed.

Following the ancient advice, Victorian doctors advocated genital massage for any woman prone to "the vapors," a collective term used to describe symptoms that included tiredness, shortness of breath, insomnia, lack of appetite, general irritability, or simply disagreeing with one's husband. The archives are full of doctors bemoaning the time spent inducing physician-assisted "paroxysm," which technically means spasm, because certain uncooperative patients took their time reaching the conclusion.

Extraordinarily, no member of the medical community realized these paroxysms were a female orgasm—apart perhaps from the patients, who for the most part proclaimed themselves to feel much better after their first treatment and immediately agreed to join the ongoing program. Consequently, gynecological massage clinics—they would be called something quite different today—sprang up all over Europe and America.

SUPPLY AND DEMAND

As the demand for such treatments grew to quite alarming proportions, doctors complained of sore fingers and wrists, quickly joining the ranks of the first acknowledged victims of repetitive strain injury (RSI). The Swiss found the solution in a handheld clockwork device that thumped adequately well. But the silly things kept running out of power just as the patients showed signs of impending paroxysm—

shortness of breath, flushing of the skin around the neck and treatment area, and sometimes grunting noises. (One can only assume not one single nineteenth-century doctor's wife enjoyed a happy sex life, because these professionals failed to recognize the patients' responses for what they really were.)

Next on the list, and slightly more successful, was hydro-percussion, which used water-jets aimed at the clitoris and brought about rapid and intense paroxysms. Unsurprisingly, it was a hit among patients, and doctors were forced to conclude that hydro-percussion induced a more powerful paroxysm, which was thus all the better for the patient. Demand increased exponentially.

However, the cost of the equipment and the fact that a room set up for such treatment was of little use for anything else put hydro-percussion out of the hands of all but the wealthiest physicians and patients. So in came the recently revived spa clinics, already in the aqua-treatment business, where doctors set up discreet centers where ladies flocked to "take the waters" twice daily for one week.

MACHINE TAKES OVER

Meanwhile, in 1868 Dr. George Taylor of New York, tired of relieving a woman's hysteria by hand—the strain brought on by the number of paroxysms he was required to induce meant he could no longer hold his golf clubs properly—devised a new solution: a treatment table that incorporated

> # MINI MYTH
> ## A SPRING IN HER STEP
>
> The famous French physician Henri Scoutetten's notes from 1843 on hydro-percussion as a remedy for "female pelvic congestion" revealed why the practice had become so popular:
>
> > The first impression produced by the jet of water is painful, but soon the effect of the percussion, the reaction of the organism to the cold, which causes the skin to flush, and the re-establishment of equilibrium all create so agreeable a sensation that it is necessary to take precautions that they do not go beyond the prescribed time, which is usually four or five minutes. After the douche, the patient dries herself off, refastens her corset, and returns with a brisk step to her room.

a steam-driven vulvar agitator that pounded away from below a durable rubber membrane.

It was an immediate hit within the medical profession. Simple to use and with minimal effort involved, all the physician had to do was to instruct his patient to lie facedown on the table with her "treatment area" positioned over the central aperture. He then fired up the device and asked the patient to make whatever minor adjustments in her position she felt necessary to the successful conclusion of the treatment. But problems with Taylor's table soon arose: It

*Somewhat cumbersome:
the vibrator and the treatment table*

was large and cumbersome, not to mention noisy, and the recipients of its attentions found it all a bit impersonal. Apparently most preferred the personal touch.

GRANVILLE'S HAMMER

The solution came in 1880 when Britain's Dr. Joseph Mortimer Granville (1833–1900) designed and patented the world's first handheld electric vibrator for clinical use. He liked to call it his "percussor," but everyone else, much to the doctor's chagrin, coined it "Granville's Hammer."

In profile the percussor resembled a cross between a hair dryer and a tool a mechanic might use to remove wheel nuts. It could be fitted with a variety of differently shaped rubber heads and was suspended from a moveable platform when not in use. And best of all, the patients loved it—they flocked to be percussed, again and again.

Although Granville himself never used it, stating in his paper "Nerve-Vibration and Excitation as Agents in the Treatment of Functional Disorder and Organic Disease" (1883): "I have never yet percussed a female patient. . . . I have avoided, and shall continue to avoid the treatment of women by percussion, simply because I do not wish to be hoodwinked, and help to mislead others, by the vagaries of the hysterical state."

In 1902 the American market responded to Granville's invention with a less industrial-looking unit for "self-treatment," sounding the death knell for a majority of the discreet gynecological massage parlors and for the medical "pelvic percussing" market. First marketed by the still-extant domestic appliance company Hamilton Beach, the handheld vibrator was the fifth domestic appliance to be electrified, after the fan, the kettle, the sewing machine, and the pop-up toaster.

On the move: the portable vibrator

A QUIVERING SUCCESS

And there was gold in them there thrills! Demand was enormous. Widely advertised in respectable publications ranging from the *Sears-Roebuck Catalogue* to the suitably named *Woman's Home Companion*, a whole variety of vibrator models were soon available to suit every budget. These ranged in power from approximately 1,000 pulses a minute on the cheap-and-cheerful models to the top-of-the-range models, including the much eulogized Chattanooga, which cost approximately $200 and delivered an eye-watering 8,000 pulses a minute.

The Chattanooga was a free-standing device, roughly 1 yard in height, with a ma-neuverable "action arm" that could be lowered to a person laying down, giving them access to the business end of the device, which was tipped with something resembling a large supposi-tory. Now stripped of their highly lucrative onanistic revenue stream, high-profile doctors fell over one an-other in the rush to market their own such devices. And

The Chattanooga

Health for Women could not recommend them enough as the only resort for those suffering from "pelvic congestion," who would soon find that "all the pleasures of youth which will once again throb within you."

NAUGHTY BUT NICE

Thousands of American and European women did indeed throb away to their hearts' content, while the menfolk twirled their waxed moustaches and continued to mutter about "women's problems." It may strike the modern reader as incredible that until only the last century thousands of ladies were routinely masturbated by doctors, while their husbands remained oblivious. But then most men, including doctors, were fairly ignorant of female sexuality. Men enjoyed sex and women tolerated it—that was the natural order of things. It is little wonder, therefore, that women popped out for the odd physician-assisted paroxysm, or invested in a Chattanooga "choo-choo" of their own.

By the 1920s medical masturbation had ceased to be prescribed, and ladies' percussers had become handheld, battery-powered devices, ultimately stripped of their thin veneer of respectability when they made regular appearances in the growing sex-film industry. And finally, in 1952, "hysteria," along with all its attendant symptoms, was removed from all official lists of recognized medical conditions.

MINI MYTH
SERIOUS BUSINESS

All this percussing was absolutely not regarded as a furtive and seedy sideline of medicine. *The Merck Manual*, still a respected doctors' guide, listed in its first edition of the twentieth century "female hysteria" as a recognized condition. "Pelvic massage," by manual or mechanical means, was recommended as the only effective treatment. And, as proof that no individual, not even at the beginning of the twentieth century, thought there might be a sexual angle to all this percussing, the same manual suggested sulfuric acid should be used to remove sensation from the clitoris of any woman who showed excessive interest in or derived "too much pleasure" from sexual arousal.

Tobacco can cure a variety of health problems.

Tobacco takes its name from an early Caribbean word for a cigar (hence the name given to the cigar-shaped island Tobago) and was first brought to Europe from the Americas in or around 1518 by the Spanish—not, as myth would have it, by Sir Walter Raleigh. When tobacco was first introduced to the West it was welcomed as a medicinal miracle that could cure much of that which ails man.

A CURE-ALL

The noxious weed was immediately touted as a wondrous herbal remedy by its importers. They regaled the Spanish and Portuguese courts with tales of the native suppliers eulogizing the benefits of tobacco smoke enemas, in particular. Although it seems a not insignificant detail was lost in translation: The native tobacco vendors in fact only used tobacco remedies to cure constipation in their horses. But with the absence of this technicality, Europeans enthusiastically adopted the practice. Smoke-enema treatments, at the time referred to as "glysters," became very popular across much of the continent and would remain so until the mid-nineteenth century.

The case for the many benefits of tobacco was significantly buoyed by the findings of the Spanish physician and botanist Nicolás Monardes (1493–1588). His book on its use in the treatment of a whole host of conditions, ranging from constipation to epilepsy, was published in three parts from 1565 to 1574. As a consequence of Monardes's

REALITY CHECK
THE FIRST SMOKING BAN

It may come as something of a surprise for anti-tobacco campaigners to learn, but Adolf Hitler was, in fact, the main driving force behind the first-ever national anti-smoking program. After Nazi doctors discovered the first proof of a link between smoking and lung cancer, and the risk smoking posed to unborn children, Hitler's regime implemented a series of strategies aimed at reducing tobacco consumption.

It was Nazi Germany that banned smoking on public transportation, in air-raid shelters, and in several public buildings and restaurants, as well as forbidding advertising that presented smoking in a positive light. Smoking was not allowed in the Luftwaffe, and SS officers were banned from lighting up while on duty.

discoveries, smoke blowing was then used to help cure a range of ills — those afflicted by earaches had tobacco smoke blown in their ears; those with sinus problems received smoke up the nose; and those with gastrointestinal problems had smoke blown in them by another route altogether.

Hard as it may be to contemplate today, from the early sixteenth century until the mid-nineteenth century, the great and the good lined up to have smoke pumped up their rear ends by a contraption that looked like a cross between a pair of fireside bellows and an incense burner. While the common man preferred to take in his tobacco smoke in a more conventional manner, those who could afford it sub-mitted themselves to smoke enemas with relish. Despite the indignity of the procedure, the trend spawned a veritable industry, complete with its own hierarchy. On the bottom rung were the "lemonaders," whose unenviable duty it was to clean out the waiting patient with lemonade before the more highly regarded "fumier" came in to do his job.

THE PROOF IS IN THE PUFFING

An incident in Oxford in December 1650 further cemented the idea that the smoke enema held supposedly miracu-lous powers. A young servant-girl called Anne Greene was wrongly accused and convicted of the murder of her own child, which had in fact been stillborn. Hanged before the obligatory yelling mob, Greene's body was taken down and carted away for dissection by would-be surgeons. During the procedure someone in the morgue thought they detected a slight twitch of Greene's fingers, so she was immediately administered a smoke enema in an attempt to revive her. It

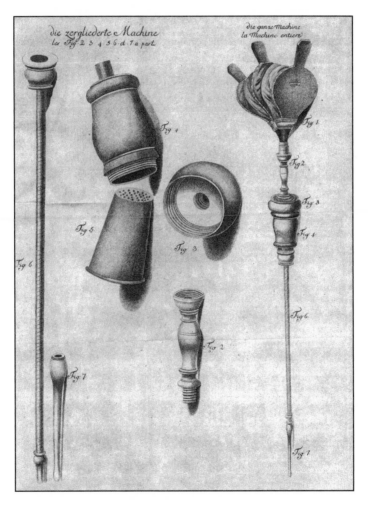

Brace yourself: the tools of the trade

was a success—she sat up in startled confusion and received a full pardon. Greene went on to become a living advertisement for the apparently wondrous powers of the treatment.

While the smoke enema treatment held sway, it was widely respected in the canon of accepted medicine. In 1774, the Society for the Recovery of Persons Apparently Drowned was formed, aimed at promoting lifesaving intervention in the case of drowning. The society used the money received from public donations to install smoke enema huts along the London reaches of the Thames and at strategic points on the city's larger lakes. Inspired by Anne Greene, the society wanted to provide people with a failsafe method of either establishing death or of resuscitating victims of near drowning. The society did in fact enjoy numerous successes and, from such unlikely beginnings, it evolved into the present-day Royal Humane Society.

MINI MYTH
ALL THAT GLISTERS . . .

Despite their surge in popularity, smoke enema treatments were not universally embraced. Shakespeare's "all that glisters is not gold" from *The Merchant of Venice* is said by some to be a pun based on the practice.

And the treatment did not catch on so well in America. The phrase "to blow smoke up someone's ass," which refers to an attempted con or deception, was coined in response to the questionable credibility of smoke enemas.

PURE POISON

Anal fumigation went into decline in the early nineteenth century as scientific research began to reveal tobacco's poisonous qualities. The English physiologist and surgeon Sir Benjamin Brodie provided the most significant research in this area when he discovered that nicotine, the principal component of tobacco, can interfere with blood circulation. Nevertheless, physicians still used tobacco smoke to treat cholera. No matter how improbable this sounds, it must be remembered that this was before the broad acceptance of germ theory, and all disease was thought to be transmitted by foul smells (malaria literally translates to "bad air"; see page 113). Free tobacco was issued following every outbreak of cholera, with all recipients, including children, required to puff away to create a fog to fight off the cholera "fumes."

MINI MYTH
Dearly Departed

The notoriety of Greene's enema also gave rise to the habit within wealthy circles of pumping the recently departed with smoke, "just to make sure"—even in death there was no escaping the smoking glyster. In the early nineteenth century, when that practice had fallen from grace, those fearful of being buried alive could have a bell-string installed in the coffin to alert graveyard attendants to their predicament.

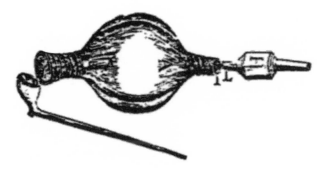

A device for administering smoke enemas

COLONICS CATCH ON

Despite the treatment's general decline by the mid-nineteenth century, smoke enemas had a lasting legacy—as the fumiers disappeared, the lowly lemonaders rose to take their place. People had grown used to, and even obsessed with, things being shoved up their backsides, and they seem to have decided that even if the smoke had to go, why not stick with the lemonade wash. Although there is evidence to suggest the Ancient Egyptians and Greeks favored such "hygiene," this was the beginning of the still-continuing and rather questionable trend for colonic irrigation—as championed by the late Princess of Wales, who apparently had a thrice weekly "royal flush," each of which involved a staggering twelve gallons of sterilized mineral water.

As a consequence of a sixteenth-century translator's inattention to detail, there exists today a multibillion-dollar industry of colonic irrigation clinics enjoyed by the modern counterparts of the smoke enema devotees. The administrators of the smoke enema could be excused for not knowing any better; they actually thought they were administering a valid treatment. The same, however, cannot be said for the modern-day irrigation lobby, which has managed to convince its patients that we are all being slowly poisoned by impacted fecal matter sticking to the inside of the large intestine.

No autopsy performed since records began has ever found evidence to support this, and the pointless and, it could be argued, dangerous practice of irrigation can cause side effects ranging from amoebic infection to internal perforations and heart failure.

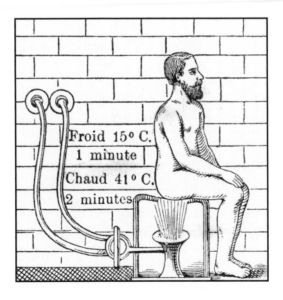

In the wake of the smoke

Injecting monkeys' glands into humans encourages sexual rejuvenation.

For centuries people, or rather men, have been searching for substances that will render women so sexually aroused that they will welcome their advances and reawaken the most listless loins. Until the invention of Viagra (although technically not an aphrodisiac) in the late twentieth century, the most famous sexual stimulant was Spanish Fly. Prepared from the wing-sheaths of the blister beetle, this aphrodisiac has been used and abused by the torpid and lusty since Roman times.

How its reputation has endured, however, is a mystery, as the closest to any aphrodisiac effect it engenders is irritation of the urinary tract, with other side effects ranging from vomiting, diarrhea, and permanent damage to the kidneys to cardiac arrhythmia and death. Far from lighting people's fires, Spanish Fly would have put a damper on any Roman orgy; and yet it is still touted in liquid and tablet form on the Internet today for those who like to live dangerously—or not at all.

*A helping hand: an aphrodisiac
containing Spanish Fly*

FOOD OF LOVE

Over the centuries, various foods have enjoyed transient notoriety for their supposed aphrodisiac effects. Sixteenth-century Spanish explorers were entranced by the pendulous avocado fruits of Mexico, especially when they were told *avocado* meant "testicle" in the local tongue. The amorous conquistadores immediately began shipping the fruits home, where they would be turned into a paste for foolish old men to apply to their genitals while sitting out in the sun. Naturally the crushed avocados failed to have the desired effect, but the Mexicans, it seems, derived no end of amusement from tales of such antics.

MINI MYTH
THE HUMBLE TOMATO

The tomato once enjoyed extended infamy as a potent aphrodisiac. The fruit was introduced to Europe by the Moors, which prompted the French to call it *pomme de Moor*. The English misheard this as *pomme d'amour*, or love apple, and leaped to the inevitable conclusion. The medieval church mounted a counterattack by suggesting the fruit was in fact poisonous.

Because the tomato plant resembles a deadly nightshade (to which it is in fact related), notions of the fruit's so-called toxicity became enshrined in medical lore. The idea became cemented in the sixteenth-century mind with the publication of John Gerard's *Herball* (1597), which condemned the plant for generations to come. Long after the Church had moved on to other concerns, the medical profession was still firmly of the opinion that anyone who ate two or three tomatoes would suffer instant death. It was not until the early to mid-eighteenth century that this idea was on the whole disproved following simple experimentation on behalf of thrill-seekers.

Americans remained convinced of the tomato's toxicity until the early nineteenth century, when, according to legend, Colonel Robert Gibbon Johnson stood on the steps of the Old Courthouse of Salem on September 26, 1820, and ate a basketful before an astonished crowd.

TESTICLE TREATMENT

The quest for sexual rejuvenation continued, soon to be appropriated by the far-from-ethical Russian-born French surgeon Serge Voronoff (1866–1951), who, along with his compatriot Ilya Ivanov (see page 133), may have been responsible for the deaths of millions of people worldwide.

In 1889, while conducting pioneering research into methods of curbing the aging process, Voronoff began to practice his methods on himself, injecting his body with extracts from ground-up dog and guinea pig testicles. The effects were barely perceptible, so Voronoff moved on to glandular tissue transplants of the same substance and published papers eulogizing it as the way forward in the fight against everything from flagging desire to schizophrenia. The international press and the European and American medical profession naively accepted Voronoff's findings without ever asking him for corroborative evidence.

In early 1920 Voronoff began transplanting the testes of executed criminals into the gullible who had cash to spare. When supply failed to keep up with demand, he began using monkey testicles, grafting thin slices of the glands into the scrotums of the rich and famous. By 1922, monkey gland treatment was the talk of the medical profession. Voronoff grew rich, not only from the operations he conducted on the likes of Kemal Atatürk, the first president of the Republic of Turkey, and other heads of state, but also from the income he generated by teaching other doctors and surgeons to expand his folly across the rest of Europe and America.

In 1923 more than 700 high-status delegates of the International Congress of Surgeons came from all over Europe and America to laud Voronoff at a conference in London and to hail him as the father of rejuvenation. However, no person in attendance seemed to notice that the master himself looked a trifle aged and balding; or if they did, no one had the courage to cry, "Physician, heal thyself!"

REALITY CHECK
IT FELT LIKE A GOOD IDEA AT THE TIME

In the late 1780s bunnies were introduced to Australia. The fox was introduced 100 years later to deal with the rabbits' expanding population—but instead of eating the rabbits, the foxes preferred to eat the sheep. Eventually, in the 1950s the bunny-killing virus myxomatosis was unleashed to undo what should never have been done in the first place.

DISAPPOINTING RESULTS

By 1930 Voronoff had packed monkey genitals into the scrotums of more than 500 wealthy patients in France alone, but he would soon overplay his hand. Diversifying into the female market, Voronoff began transplanting monkey ovaries into women who feared the onset of age. At first, women flocked to his surgery door as the carrot of lasting allure proved too strong to resist. The results were disappointing. None of Voronoff's female patients saw any discernible slow down in their natural aging. To make matters worse, many of the men Voronoff had treated in the early 1920s began to die in large numbers; dark mutterings of disillusionment and dissent grew louder.

It then became public that Voronoff had transplanted a human ovary into a female monkey and had inseminated it with human sperm. This was a step too far for his now less-than-adoring public. The hitherto sycophantic medical profession also found itself getting twitchy, and it started to shine the harsh light of skepticism, which should have been directed long before, on to Voronoff's work and claims.

By the close of the 1930s, not only were most of Voronoff's early patients six feet under—none having fathered broods of children late in life, nor having lived past any conventional age—but testosterone had been synthesized, enabling direct-injection comparison tests to be conducted. As these tests were progressing, Voronoff, knowing full well what the results would be, quietly prepared for a life of opulent retirement in Switzerland.

As Voronoff expected, none of the experiments he had claimed to have conducted on the rejuvenation of farmyard animals could be replicated. The whole charade might have been quite amusing were it not for one troublesome detail. The modern scourge of HIV is not a disease of the 1980s (see page 136) but one that first arose in the late 1920s when SIV, the simian equivalent, somehow jumped the species barrier. Not surprisingly, there are many today who work and research in that field of medicine who consider the transplanting of monkey reproductive organs into assorted humans to have been a possible vector.

The selective breeding of humans can weed out the weak from society.

Charles Darwin (1809–82) could never have foreseen the long-term ramifications of his published works. In the short term the fallout was bad enough. Denounced by members of the church who, along with other ill-informed antagonists, had not even read his work properly, Darwin was rebuked for proclaiming man is the descendant of monkeys. In reality, he had not proposed anything of the sort. In the long term, the effects were far more devastating. "Survival of the fittest," a phrase attributed to Darwin, was later used by tyrannical elements in justification of, among other oppressive policies, the new "science" of eugenics. Darwin did not invent the expression; and the man who *had* coined the phrase, the English biologist, philosopher, and sociologist Herbert Spencer (1820–1903), had in fact intended it to mean those creatures best fitted to their environment, be they weak *or* strong.

EUGENICS IS BORN

The most questionable scientific idea based on Darwin's work arose when his own cousin, Francis Galton (1822–1911) — the man who championed the use of fingerprints in criminal detection — used Darwin's work as the basis for eugenics. Derived from the Greek *eugenes* (of noble race or birth), eugenics advocated controlled breeding in an attempt to increase the chances of desirable characteristics in offspring.

Like many intellectuals, Darwin spoke before considering the repercussions. In his *The Descent of Man, and Selection in Relation to Sex* (1882) he mused on how medical and scientific advances had meant that the weaker and less productive of our species were artificially propped up to allow them to survive and breed; a harsher environment would naturally cull such parasites. At his most incendiary, Darwin suggested:

> Thus the weaker members of civilized societies propagate their kind. . . . No one who has attended to the breeding of domestic animals will doubt that this must be highly injurious to the race of man . . . but there appears to be at least one check in steady action, namely that the weaker and inferior members of society do not marry so freely as the sound; and this check might be indefinitely increased by the weak in body or mind refraining from marriage, though this is more to be hoped for than expected.

Within a matter of months of reading his cousin's book Galton had formulated his own take on the future of humanity. British society—and indeed the entire world—would benefit enormously if all such dead wood was eliminated. His *Inquiries into Human Faculty and Its Development* (1883) first coined the term *eugenics*.

Eugenics makes the world go 'round:
the front cover of America's satirical
Puck *magazine, June 1913*

GENETICS HOLDS THE KEY

It all made perfect sense: Breeding kennels always match the strongest and the smartest dog with the smartest and the best bitch, and the equine bloodstock lines had been running on the same principles for centuries. New discoveries in the science of genetics further helped Galton's case. Gregor Mendel's experiments on pea patches (see box on facing page) led to an understanding of how heredity works. When Mendel crossed pea plants with defined but opposite characteristics—for example, a long and a short stem—the result was not an average of the two heights, but a tall plant. In an outright challenge to contemporary scientific thought that believed offspring inherited a blend of their parents' characteristics, Mendel's discoveries concluded that inherited characteristics can be passed on to offspring unaltered, with the strongest predominating. Galton's eugenics applied Mendel's findings to the human race: Why not selectively breed together the very best and in the process weed out the worst of the species from the gene pool?

While Galton did not suggest that extant individuals deemed to be defective should be eliminated, he did suggest they be sterilized in order to prevent them from propagating any more of their kind. Nobility of spirit, intelligence, and artistic talent were, he decided, all inherited traits, as were fecklessness, imbecility, promiscuity, drunkenness, and criminality. To him, it would be no different to the selective breeding of dogs or thoroughbreds. Galton promised that within the span of a few generations crime and antisocial behavior would be a thing of the past and Britain would be left teeming with pleasant people who bore increasingly talented offspring.

REALITY CHECK
THE FATHER OF GENETICS

The Abbot of the Augustine Abbey of St. Thomas at Brno, Gregor Mendel (1822–84), conducted research into peas grown in the abbey grounds, and his findings awarded him the posthumous recognition as the founder of genetics. Mendel conducted his experiments between 1856 and 1863, and the results led him to devise his two laws of inheritance.

The first law (The Law of Segregation) stated that an individual possesses two alleles (a different form of a gene) for any given trait, one of which is passed on from the mother, the second from the father; whichever of these two alleles is dominant determines the character of the offspring. The second law (The Law of Independent Assortment) stated that separate genes for separate traits are passed on independently of one another. When Mendel published his results in 1866 they were met with derision. It was not until the turn of the century that the "Father of Genetics" was rediscovered.

GALTON'S SUPPORTERS

Many of the great and good of Europe and America flocked eagerly to follow Galton's banner. Notable figures including Winston Churchill and Theodore Roosevelt were open and ardent supporters of Galton's movement, as were birth control activists Marie Stopes and Margaret Sanger. Economists such as John Maynard Keynes and Sidney Webb, the cofounder of the London School of Economics, saw the financial sense of a society unfettered by the financial burden of supporting an ever-increasing number of unproductive dependants. The American proponent of moral and edible fiber, John Harvey Kellogg, was also in support of anything that improved the purity of the species. Indeed, his most famous product was initially intended to be an antimasturbation measure—a plain diet, so Kellogg thought, would dampen passionate thoughts.

LEFT-WING SUPPORT

Many today dismiss the eugenics bandwagon as an exclusively right-wing vehicle, but this was far from the case. Virtually every member of the Fabian Society, from which emerged the Labor Party, was an ardent and vocal supporter, including Irish poet and playwright W. B. Yeats (1865–1939); the leader of the British suffragette movement Emmeline Pankhurst (1858–1928); Labor Prime

Minister Ramsay MacDonald (1866–1937); and economist and social reformer William Beveridge (1879–1963).

Irish playwright and cofounder of the London School of Economics George Bernard Shaw (1856–1950) was convinced that the future of socialism lay in what he called Social Darwinism and the "selective breeding of man." The philosopher Bertrand Russell (1872–1970) went one step further when he proposed that the state should issue everyone with color-coded "procreation tickets," and anyone caught having sexual relations with a partner of a differently colored card should be given a hefty fine or even face imprisonment for "genetic treason."

Meanwhile, in America eugenics had gathered significant momentum, which would go on to influence Hitler, the man who took it to a sickeningly "logical" conclusion. But the concept of a blond-haired, blue-eyed Nordic super-race did not originate with the Führer; he derived the idea from studying the Californian eugenics program that kicked off in 1909. It was the first state to enshrine eugenics principles in its legislation, and the Californian eugenics program allowed for the enforced isolation and sterilization of unfit individuals (with the definition of "unfit" left wide open to interpretation), and marriage restriction laws. Before the eugenics program was finally eradicated in America, more than 60,000 "unfit individuals" would be forcibly sterilized and as many marriages ruled illegal, with California alone accounting for roughly one third of that total.

MINI MYTH
In Everybody's Welfare

In 1942, William Beveridge gave a report that led to the rise of the British Welfare State. As a result, he is remembered as a kindly liberal. However, the social and health institutions Britain has today bear little resemblance to the selective ones that Beveridge had in mind. While he appreciated that the state should support those unable to find work, Beveridge believed those who received benefits should lose "all citizen rights—including not only the franchise but civil freedom and fatherhood."

Beveridge's plan was for the whole state support structure to be crafted in such a way as to encourage the breeding of the middle and upper classes, who would receive far more benefits than the lower classes, who would be repressed by their own strain. On the very night his report was being debated in Westminster, Beveridge addressed the Eugenics Society to assure the nervous members that this should indeed be the result. Mercifully this was not how the report eventually went through in 1945.

CALIFORNIA DREAMING

Without the financial muscle of the Carnegie Institution, the Rockefeller Foundation, and that of countless industrial magnates, the Eugenics Program of America would have undoubtedly floundered. It also received verbal backing from a majority of the Ivy League institutions, with Stanford's president David Starr Jordan's *The Blood of the Nation* published in 1902 in support of the eugenics movement. In 1904, the Carnegie Institution began funding the Eugenics Records Office (ERO) at a laboratory complex on Long

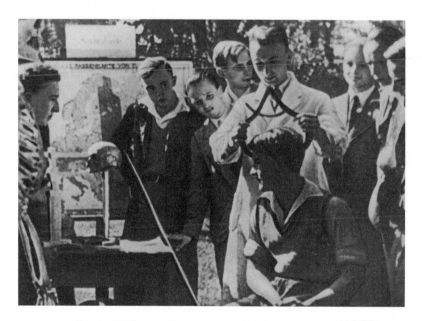

This still from the 1965 film Ordinary Fascism *shows a man's head being measured to test for Aryan qualities.*

Island. It was there that millions of index cards catalogued the lineage and identified patterns of inherited conditions of American citizens, which the ERO used to justify its often successful demands for the expansion of eugenics legislation and an intensification and broadening of the sterilization schemes. The computer technology company IBM would later copy these record-keeping methods when it developed a punch-card system to help Hitler run his own eugenics program. The infamous tattoo on concentration camp inmates' inner forearms was not just a numeric ID, it was their IBM number in which was coded race, deviancy, and skill—"Dutch, communist, carpenter," for example.

EUGENICIDE

American eugenics took a seriously dark turn with the publication in 1911 of the Carnegie-supported preliminary report by the American Breeders' Association on "The Best Practical Means for Cutting off the Defective Germ-Plasm in the Human Population." This presented an eighteen-point agendum in which point eight explored the use of euthanasia for the most hopeless of all cases. The commonly suggested form of "eugenicide" was by lethal gas chamber, a term and "solution" that would soon become all too distressingly familiar.

In 1918, Paul Popenoe (1888–1979), prominent eugenicist and US Army medical specialist in venereal diseases, coauthored *Applied Eugenics* with Roswell H. Johnson. The authors argued that, "From an historical point of view, the first method which presents itself is execution and its value in keeping up the standard of the race should not be underestimated." Popenoe was convinced that the infanticide employed in Ancient Rome and Sparta, as a birth-control method for unburdening the state of infants that showed signs of weakness or physical imperfection, was a model well worth exploring.

BUCK VS. BELL

The "science" of eugenics showed little sign of waning when in 1928 the Supreme Court chose to uphold a statute that promoted the compulsory sterilization of the unfit during the landmark case of Buck vs. Bell. The case centered on rape victim Carrie Buck (1906–83), who was impregnated by her attacker and then committed by her foster parents, John and Alice Dobbs, to the Virginia State Colony for Epileptics and the Feeble-Minded. With their own nephew the prime suspect, the Dobbs family raced to have Carrie committed as "incompetent and promiscuous," with the eugenics lobby hotly demanding she be sterilized after she gives birth. They alleged her natural mother had also been promiscuous and "sub-normal" and, although untrue, the court accepted the slur without question.

The case sat before Justice Oliver Wendell Holmes, the acclaimed physician, writer, and poet. He sanctioned the enforced sterilization, pronouncing, "It is better for all the world, if instead of waiting to execute degenerate offspring for crime, or to let them starve for their imbecility, society can prevent those who are manifestly unfit from continuing their kind. Three generations of imbeciles are enough."

This was both unfair and untrue: The child born as a result of the rape, Vivian, was a perfectly normal girl who did well at school but died, aged eight, of enteric colitis. Nevertheless, close tabs were kept on Carrie's other relatives, most probably by the ERO. Carrie's sister, Doris, was forced to undergo surgery that she was told was an appendectomy but was in fact a sterilization done in order to "terminate the family pollution of society." She did not find out the truth until she was 67.

Carrie lived into her seventies, a lifelong and avid reader, and those who found themselves partnered against her at bridge had no call to think her "feeble-minded." Justice Holmes's shameful summing up of the case was later quoted back to the American judges presiding over the Nazi Nuremberg war trials by the defendants' council.

A MATCH MADE IN HEAVEN

In 1934 the founder of the California State University at Sacramento and leading light of the Californian eugenics program, Charles M. Goethe (1875–1966), accepted an invitation from Germany to observe its developments in the area of eugenics. Although Germany's population was far smaller than that of the United States, its sterilizations by then were already exceeding 5,000 per month. Upon his return to California, Goethe gathered together his fellow eugenics committee members to congratulate them:

> You will be interested to know that your work has played a powerful part in shaping the opinions of the group of intellectuals who are behind Hitler in this epoch-making program. Everywhere I sensed that their opinions have been tremendously stimulated by American thought. I want you, my dear friends, to carry this thought with you for the rest of your lives, that you have really jolted into action a great government of 60 million people.

But the darkest link between the established American eugenics programs and Germany had in fact been forged earlier, when the Rockefeller Foundation had helped to establish the German eugenics program. The foundation had sent approximately $4 million (at today's value) in donations to several dubious German research projects; the Kaiser Wilhelm Institute for Anthropology, Human Heredity and Eugenics in Berlin was the major beneficiary.

For quite some time the American eugenics lobby had been thwarted in its dubious desires to conduct experiments on twins, but with Hitler they saw the chance to do so by proxy. On May 13, 1932, the foundation's New York office cabled its Paris counterpart with the following missive: "JUNE MEETING EXECUTIVE COMMITTEE NINE THOUSAND DOLLARS OVER THREE YEAR PERIOD TO KWG INSTITUTE ANTHROPOLOGY FOR RESEARCH ON TWINS AND EFFECTS ON LATER GENERATIONS OF SUBSTANCES TOXIC FOR GERM PLASM."

At the time, the Head of the Institute of Anthropology, Human Heredity and Eugenics was Otmar Freiherr von Verschuer (1896–1969), a man well known in American eugenics circles, and whose gruesome assistants Josef Mengele (1911–79) and Karin Magnussen (1908–1997) would later achieve their own notoriety. But it was here, under Verschuer and with Rockefeller money, that Mengele started on the road that led him to the SS and Auschwitz, and further unspeakable experiments on twins.

As World War II drew closer, the Rockefeller Foundation suspended all funding, but the Verschuer-Mengele program had by then assumed a life and will of its own. From Auschwitz, Mengele would send off all manner of tissue and blood samples from twins he had infected with diseases ranging from typhus to syphilis. To Magnussen he sent twins' eyes, especially those of any pair unlucky enough to have eyes of a different color to each other, her particular area of interest. Extraordinarily, and despite loads of evidence pointing to Verschuer and Magnussen's culpability, they were both spared prosecution as war criminals.

In July 1946 when the war was over, Popenoe and Verschuer resumed their correspondence, with the former informing the latter, "It was indeed a pleasure to hear from you again. I have been very anxious about my colleagues in Germany. I suppose sterilization has been discontinued [there]?" Some people just don't know when to give up.

Within a matter of a few years, and like so many other American and German eugenicists, Verschuer had successfully re-branded himself as a geneticist. He assumed a comfortable professorship at the University of Münster, became a valued member of the American Society of Human Genetics, and yet all the while he maintained, until his death, that he had accepted his membership to the American Eugenics Society *during* the war.

MINI MYTHS
WELL, I NEVER!
POPULAR SCIENTIFIC IDEAS DEBUNKED

- When your arm goes to sleep it is not due to inhibited blood flow.
- Eyeballs cannot be removed from their sockets for treatment and then popped back in again.
- Sugar does not make kids hyperactive.

The Earth is flat.

The theory of a flat Earth immediately brings to mind those who had derided Christopher Columbus's ambition to sail around the world by claiming he would simply sail off the edge of the Earth. In reality, very few people in Columbus's time thought the Earth was flat; the notion that it had been an accepted idea was invented in the mid-nineteenth century by the humorist Washington Irving (1783–1859) in his hugely popular book *The Life and Voyages of Christopher Columbus* (1828). Irving concocted an entirely false account of Columbus's confrontation with the Salamancan Committee, complete with fabricated quotes attributed to idiotic clerics who allegedly spouted spurious notions of a flat Earth.

As events actually transpired, the Salamancan Committee objected to what they thought was Columbus's gross underestimation of the expanse of water he was proposing to cross. They were right and Columbus was wrong — the world was twice the size of the explorer's estimations. Nevertheless, the notion of a flat Earth was both ancient and pervasive, and it is also still adhered to by some. Perhaps the inspiration for Irving's prank was the fact that the medieval Church was chock-full of diehard flat-earthers.

Columbus—with globe—before the court

ELEPHANTS AND TURTLES

Hindu cosmology suggested the Earth was a flat-bottomed dome that was carried on the back of four elephants, which in turn stood on a giant turtle that swam in an infinite ocean. The Babylonians, too, were flat-earthers. They believed the globe was a disc floating in the sea, surrounded by a rim of mountains that supported the heavens. The ancient Egyptians also believed the earth to be flat, except their version saw the earth as rectangular shaped, with Egypt, naturally enough, situated in the center.

In much the same way, during the Middle Ages early European flat-earthers believed in a flat and square Earth because the Bible (Rev. 7:1) makes reference to the four corners of the Earth, each of which was guarded by angels who controlled the four winds. This was a time when the Church reserved the right to burn alive anyone who challenged the word of the good book.

The world according to Hindu cosmology

AGAINST THE ODDS

It is difficult, with hindsight, to see how such folly was allowed to triumph over proof to the contrary. The Ancient Greeks had realized the Earth was a sphere simply by observing how inbound ships were first visible by the tip of their masts, with the rest of the vessel rising into view as it drew closer. They were extensive travelers and soon deduced that as their location changed, so, too, did their relationship to the stars, with some disappearing from view while new ones appeared. They also observed that no matter how far they sailed, the inclination all around them, from the horizons to the skies, remained the same. This cone of inclination they called the *klima*, hence "climb," and the changing weather within any one such cone was the climate. Come the Middle Ages, few with any intelligence thought the Greeks wrong, but few with a love of life were prepared to defy the Church.

Pope Gregory the Great (540–604) openly proclaimed it to be heresy to denounce the concept of a flat Earth, and as late as the sixteenth century Pope Alexander VI (1431–1503) was still maintaining the same stance. Better known as Roderic Borja, Alexander VI had no difficulty reconciling his penchant for rape and murder with his Christian ethics but, although a somewhat savvy and hand-to-throat political survivor, Borja lacked intelligence.

He was also pretty greedy, and by 1493 he had wearied of the two leading Catholic nations, Spain and Portugal, fighting each other over new territories during the Age of Discovery—while the countries fought between themselves they were failing to fill Borja's Vatican coffers. As a dedicated flat-earther, Borja decided to draw a line down the map (the first to be called a Demarcation Line) and pronounced that the Portuguese hunt to the east of the line and the Spanish to the west. (The line cut through South America, which is why Portuguese is spoken in Brazil, and Spanish elsewhere.) But it never occurred to Borja that the Portuguese could simply keep sailing east to end up in the west.

MINI MYTH
JUDGMENT DAY

Flat-earthers were not all on the Catholic side of the fence. Although the German monk Martin Luther (1483–1546) today enjoys a reputation as a gentle, pious, and measured man, he was in fact a deeply unpleasant and small-minded anti-Semite who thought that all Jews should be covered in excrement and whipped out of town; he thought, too, that the poor and downtrodden should be treated no better because that is what God intended. Having an extremely small-minded perspective, Luther was also a flat-earther. His reasoning stemmed from the fact that all humanity was destined to witness the Second Coming on Judgment Day, and, if the earth were a sphere, the view of the majority of the planet's population would be obscured.

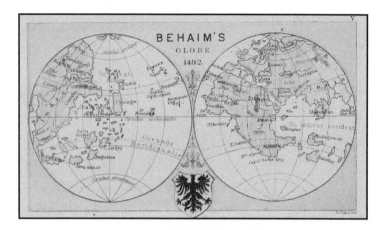

This illustration of a globe, dated 1492,
rejects the theory of a flat earth.

DETRACTORS IN THE MIDST

One of the few who dared to speak out against the flat-earth theory was Portuguese explorer Ferdinand Magellan (1480–1521), who, prior to embarking on his famous circumnavigation of 1519, pronounced, "The Church says the earth is flat but I have seen its shadow on the Moon and I have more faith in that shadow than I do in the Church." Having spoken so boldly, he had the presence of mind to board his ship and set sail. Eventually, as circumnavigations became more frequent, the Vatican was forced to admit that perhaps the earth was a sphere. Flat-earth thinking staggered on in a few fringe fundamentalist groups, mainly in America, but strange concepts of the form and profile of the Earth were not dead—even in the twentieth century.

JUMPING ON THE BANDWAGON

Far from being a rational man, Hitler, too, explored the flat-earth theory (as well as, quite conversely, the hollow-earth theory; see page 147) and finally decided that, although not flat, the earth was perhaps concave. He believed humanity ran around, upside down, on the interior of the surface, much like an army of ants. To explore this notion he ordered the German-born scientist Wernher von Braun (1912–77) to fire a series of rockets at a 45-degree angle in order to see if they landed in Australia. As the church of old had been before him, Hitler was by this point very much in charge, so von Braun nodded solemnly and set out on the doomed mission. Naturally hestitant to report his failure to hit Down Under, von Braun gently guided the Führer to the notion that, while the theory of a flat Earth may well be correct, the

An artistic representation of Columbus's arrival at Margarita Island in 1498

rockets did not contain the power necessary to validate it. Hitler seemed appeased, and von Braun made a sharp exit. But the Führer's fascination did not end there.

In April 1942, Hitler organized another attempt to prove himself right. Under the leadership of Dr. Heinz Fischer, a specialist in the field of infrared rays, an expedition was dispatched to Rügen Island in the Baltic Sea to attempt the same experiment, but this time with the aid of radar. For weeks on end the radar scanned at a 45-degree angle but nothing came back, leaving Fischer and his team extremely nervous about returning home. But they did not have to worry; by this time Hitler's attentions had been diverted to the invasion of Russia, which allowed the members of the expedition to slip quietly back into Germany unnoticed.

MINI MYTH
THE FINAL FRONTIER: SPACE GETS SILLY

Space was once home to the following nutty theories:

- Canals exist on Mars.
- The moon is a hollow vessel.
- The universe is static and does not expand.
- The hypothetical planet Vulcan orbits between Mercury and the sun.
- A full moon causes lunacy (see box on page 158).

Humans can be influenced by subliminal messaging.

Of all the discredited theories described in *They Got It Wrong: Science*, the one explored in this chapter is not only the most modern, it is also the most responsible for encouraging spin-offs of spurious science than any other notion.

MAD MEN

America during the late 1950s was a consumer's temple in which marketing men served as high priests. In 1957, market researcher James Vicary (1915–77) arrived on the scene, holding aloft the invisible Holy Grail of advertising.

Vicary reported the incredible successes he claimed he had achieved in conducting covert experiments in a public cinema in Fort Lee, New Jersey, in the summer of that same year. Vicary quite logically reasoned that consumers possessed a personal level of in-built sales resistance. He suggested that while their hearts may want the product, the ad-man's greatest enemy—the consumer's brain—was sitting in ultimate control, warning the owner. So, argued Vicary, why not cut the conscious brain out of the equation?

Vicary claimed that over a period of sixteen weeks he had exposed 45,000 cinema-goers to doctored versions of whichever film they had gone to watch. Using a tachisto-scope, an instrument used to display an image for a brief pe-riod, Vicary had incorporated flash-images that instructed audiences to "drink Coke" and "eat popcorn." Supporting his research with genuine science as to how fast the human eye can capture images and why, Vicary informed Madison

Hungry? Eat popcorn:
a mock-up of Vicary's experiment

Avenue ad gurus that his images endured for 1/3000 of a second—too fast for the eye and the conscious brain to notice, but detectable nonetheless on a subliminal level.

Because the brain had been influenced on an almost hypnotic level, no defensive actions had been activated. The result, claimed Vicary, had been an increase in the lobby sales of Coke and popcorn: They had risen by 18 percent and 57 percent, respectively. American manufacturers were agog; it all seemed to make perfect sense. The commercial worth of the carrot dangled before their collective eyes was deemed to be inestimable.

MINI MYTH
LIGHTS, CAMERA, ACTION: PHYSICS-GONE-WRONG IN THE MOVIES

- Victims of gunfire shots would never be flung backward because every action has an equal and opposite reaction.

- There is no such thing as a silencer that can reduce the noise of a gunshot to a muted *phut*.

- Quicksand does not cause drowning, because it's hundreds of times more buoyant than the Dead Sea.

- People ejected into space don't explode or experience boiling of the blood.

POLITICAL TWIST

Others, too, were excited by the possibilities offered by Vicary's discoveries, although their agendas hid an altogether more sinister edge. Political parties debated the possibility of using such tactics not only in their own television broadcasts but also during popular shows that were unrelated to politics.

There was a sudden and undignified scramble in the political arena as vast salaries were offered as incentives to entice opinion makers and so-called Depth Men (psychological manipulators) away from their Madison Avenue desks and up to Capitol Hill. Journalist Vance Packard published his still-famous *The Hidden Persuaders* (1957), which linked Washington's use of commercial advertising tactics to Vicary's experiment. Science fiction author Aldous Huxley told anyone who would listen that his *Brave New World* (1931) had come to hideous life, with Vicary "sounding the death knell of free will." And, as the debate over the ethicality of subliminal messaging rose to fever pitch, Richard Condon published *The Manchurian Candidate* (1959). A thriller that features the brainwashing of individuals by political parties, Condon's novel fanned the flames of conspiracy.

BRAINWASHING

Vicary could not have picked a better time for his fraud — for fraud is what it was — as America was still smarting from recent revelations that had emerged after the Korean War (1950–53). The sensationalist writer Edward Hunter's *Brain-washing in Red China* (1951)—which introduced the term "brainwashing" to the American people—induced paranoia among Americans by presenting images of shadowy Fu Manchu–like characters manipulating the minds of American POWs.

In reality, there had been no mind-bending experiments—apart from the CIA's notorious Project MK-Ultra (see below)—Hunter was simply weaving a web of lies. In truth, the Chinese did run re-educational programs for any prisoner who wanted to attend. Referred to as *szu-hsiang-kai-tsao*, or thought reform after mind cleansing, these programs were an attempt to rid the POWs' minds of their preconceived notions of Communist China and replace those "Western lies" with "the truth." There were no drugs, no hypnotists, no beatings; just boring lessons. That said, more than 2,000 POWs refused repatriation to America after the war, and America therefore needed to believe they had been induced to do so by indomitable means rather than by choice.

A SINISTER TURN

Perhaps unsurprisingly, the CIA, too, was more than a little interested in Vicary's experiments. In their postwar, clandestine Operation Paperclip (authorized by President Truman in 1945), the CIA had spirited back to America numerous Nazi scientists and doctors, some of whom had used death camp inmates in various psychotropic and sensory-deprivation experiments in their own attempts to achieve total mind control. More than thirty war criminals were given new identities and employed in the setup of the decidedly sinister MK-Ultra program, which used unwitting members of the public in a series of dangerous and, in some cases, lethal psychotropic experiments.

The program was petering out by 1957, but it seems that Vicary unwittingly breathed new life into it. A recently released CIA report dated January 17, 1958, conjectured:

> It might be that in order to lessen the resistance of an individual to the hypnotic induction process, the use of subliminal projection may be considered. This technique has achieved success in commercial advertising, as "eat popcorn" or "drink Coke" projected in certain movie theaters for 1/3000-of-a-second intervals. It may be that subliminal projection can also be utilized in such a way as to feature a visual suggestion such as "Obey [deleted]," or "Obey [deleted]"—with similar success.

THE LID IS LIFTED

The 1952 production of an animated version of George Orwell's *Animal Farm* had been a CIA-funded initiative and flash-messaged re-screenings were organized, but the experiment failed to yield any results. And while the CIA remained in a state of confused frustration in their attempts to manipulate whole cinema audiences into a certain frame of mind, or to undertake certain actions immediately on leaving the auditoria, American and Canadian broadcasting networks were equally unsuccessful in their own attempts to replicate Vicary's results.

The most publicized of these independent experiments was carried out by the Canadian Broadcasting Corporation during its much-viewed Sunday night show *Close Up*. During the program, invitations to the viewers to phone in to the station were flashed on the screen nearly 400 times, but the station did not receive a single call.

The next nail in the subliminal-message coffin was hammered home by Dr. Henry C. Link, director of the Psychological Corporation. He invited Vicary to demonstrate the supposedly incredible power of his technique under controlled conditions, with Vicary failing on all fronts.

Then, in 1958, Stuart Rogers, a student of psychology at New York's Hofstra University, visited Fort Lee, the home of Vicary's original experiment, to ask some very direct questions that had not yet been asked. When Rogers spotted the small local cinema where Vicary had carried out his experiment he was immediately struck by its size—it was much too small to have accommodated the numbers claimed by Vicary over the indicated time span. After an interrogation from Rogers, the manager of the cinema admitted that no such experiments had taken place.

MINI MYTH
THE ANGELS OF MONS

As the case of James Vicary suggests, once a nation has taken an idea to heart, it becomes very difficult to persuade its members otherwise. Much the same happened to the British writer Arthur Machen, whose creations spawned the legend of the Angels of Mons. The entirely fictitious story described how a host of angels protected British soldiers on the World War I battlefields, holding back the crazed Huns with flaming swords and arrows. Although it was only a story, hordes of troops, officers, and chaplains, both Allied and German, claimed to have witnessed the event for themselves. Machen's reward for trying to remind the nation that it was but a whim of his own invention was a horsewhipping from an outraged bishop who collared him on Oxford Street.

CARRYING ON REGARDLESS

Finally, in 1962, Vicary himself admitted that it had been a scam: There was no such thing as subliminal messaging. He had invented it all in an attempt to save his failing consultancy. Despite these revelations, the bandwagon Vicary had so deftly put in motion refused to listen.

No matter how loud or how often Vicary protested that subliminal messaging was nothing more than a scam, the world failed to listen. Studies conducted in 2006 show that in America today, more than 80 percent of people—including those who work in advertising or teach psychology—still believe in the sinister power of subliminal messaging. Current opinion was certainly bolstered by the author Wilson Bryan Key (1925–2008), who during the 1970s and the 1980s became the self-styled guardian against such evils.

Despite impressive academic credentials, including a PhD in communications and a membership to Mensa, Key

MINI MYTH
666 OR 616?

Did you know that the original "number of the beast" is 616, not 666? Many new testament manuscripts refer to the number 666, but in older Greek texts it's 616. Movies, TV shows, and rock albums that have used 666 to symbolize evil may have been misled.

was a firm believer in the power of subliminal messaging. He claimed that three of the ice cubes in a Gilbey's Gin ad contained the letters S, E, and X discernible within their structure; he even saw the same word if the perforations along the edge of Ritz Crackers were joined together. Key stood watch for the Christian Right lobby, forcing the multinational product company Procter & Gamble to abandon its logo of a grey-bearded man posing as a moon because he claimed the figure "666," the number of the Beast (see box on facing page), was discernible in his facial hair.

ROCK 'N' ROLL SUICIDE

But still the corrupt legacy of James Vicary rolled on. Buoyed by the success of their farcical crusade against Procter & Gamble, the subliminal watchdogs turned their attention to Gothic-themed heavy rock groups. As far as Wilson Key was concerned, there had to be subliminal hooks somewhere in the equation to help explain the attraction of their blasphemous decadence. He reasoned that there must be a call to join the ranks of Satan in the words when played backward (backmasking). Naturally, everyone started playing their record collections backward, and the Christian Right believed this to have been the cause behind many teenage suicides, after the victims received "subliminal" orders to take their own lives.

So, according to Key and his like, not only was the brain

able to see images that normally escape the human eye, it could also listen to a record played normally, log the entire performance, and then play it in reverse in order to pick up any hidden subliminal message that may have been lurking in the lyrics. Quite a mental feat. Basically, no one wanted to accept the obvious: Teenagers who filled themselves up with drugs and were given to the darkness of goth-rock culture might simply be predisposed to self-harm. But matters came to a head with the suicide of American teenager Raymond Belknap and the attempted suicide of his friend James Vance on December 23, 1985.

Both young men had a history of drug abuse and depression and had allegedly spent the day smoking marijuana and listening to hours of music by the British heavy metal band Judas Priest. They then wandered off to a graveyard where Belknap blew his head off with a shotgun, leaving Vance to try the same; he survived but with horrific injuries. Wilson Key was trotted out as a professional witness on the power of subliminal messaging for a trial in which the rock group was charged with the notion that their track "Better By You, Better Than Me" carried embedded subliminal messages that had urged the boys to take their tragic actions.

Fortunately, the judge was not that gullible, and with Key's pronouncements discounted, the case was dismissed. As Judas Priest's lead singer, Rob Halford, would wryly observe after the case, "If I'd thought that sort of crap worked, we would have embedded messages telling everyone to go out and buy more of our records."

SPURIOUS SPIN-OFFS

The gullibility of the public at large is indeed an awesome market force. One might assume that if premise B is built on premise A, which is later proved to be a complete lie, then premise B would automatically go into the garbage can of history, along with its progenitor. Not so. Despite Vicary's very public admission that subliminal messaging had been a lie, spurious spin-offs had already been set well in motion.

Although the idea of sleep-learning had been quashed in 1956 with the electroencephalography studies conducted by Charles Simon and William H. Emmons of the Rand Corporation, Vicary's lie breathed new life into the notion. Commercial ventures sprang up across America and Europe, trumpeting the false promise of allowing us to tap into the fearsome powers hidden in the subconscious—if subliminal influence could exert such power when the subject was awake, its power would be even greater if the subject was asleep. It is just a pity there is no truth in the idea.

A multibillion-dollar industry has been built on the idea of sleep-learning, which—despite having been roundly debunked by prominent sleep experts and psychologists—

still refuses to go away. In studies conducted in 1991 participants were told that personal enhancement messages would be played to them while they slept to help make them more assertive. On waking, many participants did indeed proclaim themselves to feel more in control and behaved accordingly—despite having been subjected to messages telling them to be more humble and self-deprecating. In all such experiments, conducted under clinical conditions with the subjects wired up to an EEG to ensure they really were asleep, the knowledge impartation has been nil.

THE MOZART EFFECT

From subliminal messaging and sleep-learning stemmed the "Mozart Effect," a term coined in 1991 by the French ear, nose, and throat (ENT) specialist Dr. Alfred A. Tomatis (1920–2001). Tomatis claimed that listening to certain types of music was beneficial to certain conditions and conducive to the achievement of certain objectives, and he recommended Mozart to aid depression and concentrate the mind of those with learning difficulties to the task at hand.

Tomatis's international standing was so great that two University of California heavyweights, Dr. Frances Rauscher and Dr. Gordon Shaw, looked into the alleged phenomenon and published their results in the scientific journal *Nature*. For reasons only they could conjecture—perhaps concentrating on the music helped the mind to warm up—subjects who listened to Mozart before certain tests did indeed do better than those who had been left in silence.

The good doctors said they detected a slight and very transient improvement in participant's spatial-temporal reasoning powers and that "there appear to be pre-existing sites in the brain that respond to specific frequencies." They made no mention of individual participants' IQs, nor that other experiments had reported similar findings using the music of Meatloaf and Iron Maiden. Predictably the press reported that listening to Mozart makes your children smarter—the so-called Mozart effect was ripe for exploitation.

Despite Shaw and Rauscher protesting that their work had been completely misrepresented—that there was no correlation between the playing of Mozart and the listener's intelligence—the idea had been set in motion. In 1998 the governors of both Georgia and Tennessee announced programs to provide every newborn baby with music CDs, and new research was conducted into the awareness of the unborn child. Millions of mothers-to-be snapped up devices comprised of a CD player and an implement that resembled a reverse-stethoscope to bombard their unborn with Mozart, along with recordings of their own voices making positive affirmations of life. However, Georgia and Tennessee failed to become the cradles of *wunderkind*, and we have yet to read of the first child to launch into a rendition of *Don Giovanni* as the doctor slaps it into life.

MINI MYTHS
WELL, I NEVER!
POPULAR SCIENTIFIC IDEAS DEBUNKED

- We use all of our brains (well, at least some of us do!) and not just the 10 percent of myth.
- There is no harm in waking up a sleepwalker; in fact, it is best to do so.
- Leprosy cannot be transmitted by casual contact.
- 20/20 vision does not denote perfect eyesight, only that both eyes function normally at a twenty-foot range.

Cocaine and heroin can cure a range of man's ills.

Long before they were recognized as Class-A drugs, capable of destroying the lives of those who grow, import, and consume them, cocaine and opium were hailed as panaceas by the nineteenth-century medical profession. Eulogized as cures for a range of ills, the drugs were made readily available in numerous over-the-counter products, many of which were sponsored by leading doctors and prominent figures.

THE TREND CATCHES ON

Pope Leo XIII (1810–1903) never ventured far without a hip flask of the cocaine-laced French wine Vin Mariani; he even bestowed the Vatican Gold Medal on the manufacturers and allowed his image to be used in the promotion of the product, which was marketed to ailing children, pregnant women suffering from morning sickness, or those feeling just a little under the weather. At that time, everyone

Cocaine-infused Vin Mariani:
the Pope's favorite

thought opium and cocaine to be of great benefit to mankind at large.

Mothers were also encouraged to use either drug to treat teething babies. Since the sixteenth century, misguided physicians had believed in the efficacy of slitting the gums of infants to help ease the emergence of the first teeth. The practice had gone into decline by the end of the eighteenth century, mainly for the distress it caused, but a century on it enjoyed a comeback as the pain of the incision could be followed with a direct application of one of these new "miracle anesthetics," after which no doubt the child just sat there chuckling.

With the medical profession trumpeting their merits, not to mention profiting from their mass production and sale, cocaine- and opium-based products were readily available; even grocers and clothing stores kept stocks for anyone caught short. And the hallmark of cynical advertising was all pervasive. All such drugs were recommended by an avuncular-looking medical consultant, sold under innocuous-sounding names such as Mrs. Winslow's Soothing Syrup or Professor MacGuire's Infant's Panacea. The entire medical profession was united in the opinion that opiates and cocaine were valuable cures that contained no addictive qualities. But the medical professionals paid to investigate the nature of the two drugs were in fact voracious consumers themselves, so it was little wonder that their findings completely exonerated the drugs of any charges regarding their capacity to addict.

*Soothing syrup for children: Mrs. Winslow gives
her seal of approval*

MINI MYTH
IF FREUD SAID IT'S OK . . .

The Austrian neurologist Sigmund Freud (1856–1939) championed cocaine not only as the ideal cure for opium and alcohol addiction but also as an appetite stimulant for those with anorexia and as a first-line treatment for asthma sufferers.

In *Über Coca* (1884) Freud applauded the drug's efficacy in stimulating "exhilaration and lasting euphoria, which in no way differs from the normal euphoria of the healthy person." Warming to his theme, Freud continued:

> You perceive an increase of self-control and possess more vitality and capacity for work. In other words, you are simply normal, and it is soon hard to believe you are under the influence of any drug.
>
> Long intensive physical work is performed without any fatigue. This result is enjoyed without any of the unpleasant after-effects that follow exhilaration brought about by alcohol. Absolutely no craving for the further use of cocaine appears after the first, or even after repeated taking of the drug.

BEST OF BRITISH

Queen Victoria, on her physicians' advice, guzzled laudanum, a whole-opium tincture; she took cannabis for her menstrual pains; and, like her prime minister, William Gladstone, she also liked the occasional snort of cocaine. It is probably no exaggeration to say that, throughout the greater part of the nineteenth century, the British ruling class and half of the population lived in a drug fog. And why not? The government in Victoria's day was the most aggressive drug cartel the world has yet seen. They even made the Colombian warlords look like amateurs. The UK's domestic imports of raw opium in 1830 had been alarming enough—just short of 100,000 one-pound blocks; by 1860 this had rocketed to just under 300,000 pounds.

It was the British who so dramatically expanded the poppy fields of Northern India and Afghanistan, the deadly results of which still reverberate today. Desperate to find new markets, the British Empire targeted China, despite the country's already serious opiate problem, with a total of approximately 2 million addicts. Regardless, taking advantage of the opportunity, the British began shipping great quantities of the drug to expand that user base. When the Chinese objected and demanded the trade cease, the good Victorians attacked Canton, the means by which China controlled trade with the West, in the First Opium War (1839–42).

The British emerged victorious and demanded from

China a host of concessions in the Treaty of Nanking, which included ceding Hong Kong to Queen Victoria. The Chinese were reluctant to adhere to all of the treaty's terms, leading the British to initiate another attack in the Second Opium War (1856–60). The British again emerged victorious. They added Kowloon to their previous acquisition, forced the Chinese to legalize an opium trade that was destroying their people, and began the wholesale transportation of "indentured Chinese laborers" (slaves, in other words) to the Americas to toil on the railways. China had no choice, and within a matter of years the British government had acquired over 100 million opium customers in China alone.

MINI MYTH
MEDICINE MEN:
WHEN DOCTORS GOT IT WRONG

The following list of dubious medical procedures suggests the men of medicine haven't always got it right.

- Trepanation (drilling a hole in the skull) to cure all manner of ills.
- Lobotomies to "calm" the mentally ill.
- An insulin-induced coma to relieve the symptoms of schizophrenia.
- Hysterectomies to cure paranoia in women.

HOUSTON, WE HAVE A PROBLEM

The situation in America was no better. A staggering 10 million opium pills and more than 3 million ounces of other opiate preparations were dished out to the Union Army alone during the Civil War (1861–65). While the drugs may have helped the troops to get through the horrors of war, when the conflict was over and nearly 500,000 opium-habituated troops returned to civilian life, the medical profession was forced to acknowledge that the unrestricted use of such drugs might be somewhat of a problem.

Those who could afford to fund their habit could buy the drugs locally over the counter or through mail-order from medical suppliers who still upheld the common belief that these were harmless substances, even if put to recreational use. It was the antics of those who could *not* afford their habit that first gave cause for concern.

Backed by the American Medical Association, the Society for the Suppression of the Opium Trade renewed its attack on doctors who considered opiates and cocaine to be not only harmless but also broadly beneficial. In 1893, a Royal Commission on Opium was reluctantly convened to investigate. But this was a venture doomed from the start. Although the commission went through the correct channels, listened attentively to countless witnesses, and produced a suitably weighty report, it concluded that the use of opium was not responsible for a decline in moral standards or physical damage to the user. In fact, it decreed that opium in recreational use was no worse than alcohol, and that it had positive medical benefits.

The preeminent British medical journal *The Lancet* welcomed the findings, commenting that they "dealt a crushing blow to the anti-opium faddists whose claims were either ridiculously exaggerated or wholly unfounded." The problem with the commission was that it was a *Royal* Commission and, as such, directly answerable to the junkie-in-chief herself—and no one involved relished the prospect of confronting Queen Victoria with the realities of her own laudanum and cocaine usage.

MINI MYTH
DENS OF INIQUITY

Novels promoted the myth of opium dens run by Chinese immigrants, who supposedly teemed in London's Limehouse district. While the Chinese certainly ran opium parlors in American cities where they had been transported following the Second Opium War, the Chinese population was never more than a few hundred in nineteenth-century London. There is in fact no evidence of any such dens. Why go to a seedy den in a dangerous part of London when you could buy your stash in Mayfair?

STRAIGHT TO USER

Literature began to explore the sleazy and debilitating side of opium, with Conan Doyle's Dr. Watson expressing serious disapproval of Sherlock Holmes's use of a substance detrimental to his superior intellectual powers.

But few wanted to listen to the dissenting voices on the ill effects of opiates and cocaine, and the medical profession

An artistic representation of one of London's fabled opium dens

vehemently defended its stance. In 1885 the American pharmaceutical company Parke-Davis augmented its cocaine product range with a solution that could be injected directly into the user's veins. It was sold in a variety of main-street shops, complete with syringe and backed by an advertising campaign that claimed it would "supplant the need for food, make cowards brave, make the timid loquacious and render the user insensitive to pain."

SERVING THE MASS MARKET

In 1898 the German pharmaceutical company Bayer synthesized a new and highly addictive opioid, which they marketed as an over-the-counter product under the brand name of Heroin, for the supposed heroic feelings it engendered in

Over-the-counter: one of German pharmaceutical
company Bayer's heroin products

the user. Again, the medical profession welcomed this advance without question and advocated the use of heroin for the treatment of colds and flu, bronchitis, whooping cough, and for pregnant women suffering from morning sickness.

Developments continued in America, where Confederate veteran doctor John Stith Pemberton (1831–88) invented a new cocaine-laced wine to rival Pope Leo XIII's favorite, Vin Mariani. First marketed as Pemberton's Brain Tonic, this lethal mix of alcohol and cocaine proved very popular, until 1886 when Pemberton's hometown of Atlanta, Georgia, objected to its alcohol content, forcing the doctor to create a Temperance-friendly version. It was this blend of cocaine-laced syrup and soda water that evolved into Coca-Cola. But the manufacturer became increasingly uneasy about the drug element in response to the growing notion in the South that cocaine usage was driving black men to rape white women. In 1903 all traces of cocaine had been stripped from the drink.

NEW GAME IN TOWN

By then the writing was on the wall for the continued free availability of cocaine and heroin. It had dawned on the majority of the medical profession that the unchecked use of these drugs was not the answer to the people's minor ailments. That said, the possession and use of cocaine remained unlegislated in America until 1970.

More than just a thirst quencher:
Coca Cola was advertised as a
stimulant to help relieve exhaustion.

Meanwhile, by the 1950s the Americans had taken to heart another "harmless" drug—amphetamine. Doctors on both sides of the Atlantic scattered these pills like confetti. Apparently they found them very useful to perk up patients in hospital, and everyone was buying Benzedrine inhalers over the counter. Throughout the 1950s, Pan-Am's in-flight courtesy packs for passengers included a Benzedrine inhaler, which the accompanying pamphlet advised "would make the flight more pleasant and seem to pass more quickly." No kidding!

Disease is caused by foul smell and lack of personal hygiene.

Known by many as the father of germ theory, the French chemist and microbiologist Louis Pasteur (1822–95) conducted a series of experiments in the second half of the nineteenth century that conclusively proved germs cause disease. Before Pasteur's discoveries, the overwhelming majority of the medical and scientific communities, including pioneering nurse Florence Nightingale (1820–1910), had publicly ridiculed the idea that organisms undetectable to the human eye could invade the body, breed in sufficient numbers, and bring about the death of the host.

MAKING A STINK

Until Pasteur's irrefutable evidence was published, the "miasma theory" held sway. This concept maintained that all disease was caused by foul smells, lack of personal hygiene, and, to a lesser extent, impurity of the mind and soul. Florence Nightingale certainly adhered to this notion. Her complicity may have caused thousands of deaths in the Crimea, where she thought that clean surroundings and regular Bible readings would put a patient on the road to recovery.

Back in the sixteenth century the infection theory was once advanced. The Italian physician Girolamo Fracastoro (1478–1553) believed that infective agents called spores were responsible for the spread of germs and viruses; he warned that these spores could transfer infection by direct or indirect means. He also wrote that "such things as clothes, linen, etc., which although not themselves corrupt, can nevertheless foster the essential seeds of the contagion and thus cause infection." Although Fracastoro was on the right track, it was to be approximately another 300 years before the Italian physician Agostino Bassi (1773–1856) made the first identification of living organisms as the cause of disease.

GERMINATION

In 1835, Italian silk production was in danger of collapse because the silkworms had fallen prey to an invasion of parasitic mites. Bassi made note of the white, powdery coating of spores found on the dead and dying silkworms, and he became the first to make the correct connection between infective invasion and disease. Thirty years later, when the French silk industry fell prey to the same parasite, Louis Pasteur, inspired by the work of Bassi, came to the same conclusion, although, in Pasteur's defense, he had

MINI MYTH
BY THE POWER OF GOD . . .

Before the miasma theory gained ground, the majority of the Ancient civilizations believed disease to be a punishment inflicted by the gods. Although detractors did exist: *Atharvaveda*, the sacred Hindu text written toward the end of the second millennium BCE, suggested living causative agents were responsible for disease; although the text did not elaborate on the size and nature of the agents, so it may have been nothing more than guesswork.

Marcus Terentius Varro (116–27 BCE), a Roman physician and polymath, was the next to suggest something more than bad air and foul smells might be responsible for disease. Not only did he caution people against building homes near swamps, he even suggested they refrain from frequenting them, because proliferating therein were "certain minute creatures that cannot be seen by the eyes, which float in the air and enter the body through the mouth and nose and there cause serious diseases." But few paid attention to Marcus Terentius; majority opinion held the gods to be responsible.

by that point already made major inroads into the discovery of germ theory.

As Bassi had before him, Pasteur recommended the separation of the colonies of silkworms into disinfected farms and the immediate destruction of any silkworm that showed

LE CHOLÉRA

*This front page of a French newspaper from 1912
depicts Death carrying cholera.*

signs of infection. Despite these quarantines and precautions having twice eradicated the epidemic, the medical and scientific communities were not prepared to listen. The majority of opinion still held that all disease—cholera, typhoid, malaria, to name only a few—was the inevitable progeny of foul smells. In Austria, Pasteur's contemporary Ignaz Semmelweis (1818–65) was also leading a case against miasma theory, but so vehement were his attacks that it would eventually lead to his murder by a group of some of the most prominent medical figures in Austrian medicine.

PLEASE WASH YOUR HANDS

Death rates of approximately 20 percent for mothers and offspring during childbirth were considered quite normal in some clinics in the mid-nineteenth century. This included the First Obstetrical Clinic in a Viennese hospital, which offered benefits to expectant mothers if they volunteered themselves as guinea pigs for new doctors.

There were two maternity clinics at the hospital. Semmelweis took up his position as senior resident at the First Obstetrical Clinic in 1846 but was puzzled to find that the childbirth death rate at the Second Clinic was a mere 2 percent—18 percent lower than the First Clinic. The only difference between the two institutions was that no autopsies were conducted at the Second Clinic. His second clue came from the patients themselves. Having noticed that something was seriously awry at the First Clinic, a good number of Vienna's pregnant women contrived to give birth en route to the First Clinic so they could still get the benefits promised by the program without having to run the gauntlet of its professional care.

Semmelweis was staggered to find that the death rate in this forward-thinking group was almost nonexistent.

Semmelweis's predictions were confirmed with the sudden death of his good friend, professor of forensics Jakob Kolletschka, in 1847. Kolletschka had been supervising a student conducting an autopsy on a patient who had died of puerperal (childbirth) fever in the First Clinic, and within three days of being nicked by a carelessly brandished scalpel, he was himself dead of the same condition.

Focusing his attentions on the autopsy rooms, the first thing Semmelweis noted was that students and professors

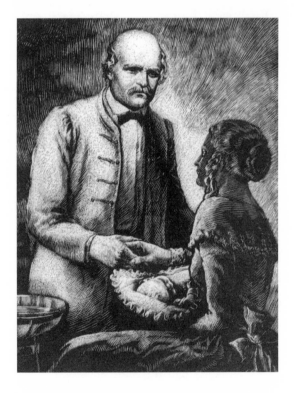

Ignaz Semmelweis with mother and child

routinely left them without washing and headed straight to the treatment and examination rooms. He immediately instituted a regime of hand washing in a solution of chlorinated lime, and the death rate fell by 90 percent overnight. Within two months it was nil. However, instead of being hailed a hero, Semmelweis was harassed out of his post by colleagues offended at being ordered to wash their hands like naughty schoolboys. What possible correlation could there have been between the hand-washing fiasco and the fall in the death rate?

MINI MYTHS
WELL, I NEVER!
POPULAR SCIENTIFIC IDEAS DEBUNKED

- Edison did not invent the lightbulb.
- Benjamin Franklin did not invent the so-called Franklin stove.
- Pythagoras did not come up with "his" eponymous theorem.
- The Wright brothers were not the first to achieve powered flight.
- Alexander Bell was not responsible for inventing the telephone.

THE COLD SHOULDER

When Semmelweis left the clinic, the death rate returned to its original position. In every subsequent post he took up, Semmelweis instituted the same hand-washing regime and the death rate plummeted, but his old enemies had him pushed out of every subsequent position he assumed — and the death rate rose in his wake. And *still* nobody listened. Unbelievably, the Viennese Medical Council saw Semmelweis as a troublemaker who was intent on blaming patient and infant death on some of its more influential members. The same members who felt it was their right to poke around inside patients with hands still dripping with germs.

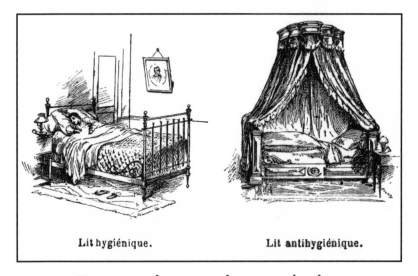

Lit hygiénique.　　　　　　Lit antihygiénique.

From an early twentieth century book on
the new rules of hygiene. The bed on the right was
thought to trap germs.

Ridiculed as a fractious oddball, Semmelweis was cut out of the medical fraternity and marginalized. But he remained unrepentant. Continuing his campaign in exile, Semmelweis published an open letter to the obstetrics fraternity at large, which was, unfortunately for its sender, a little on the antagonistic side. Feeling that decisive action was needed, Semmelweis's enemies decided to have him declared insane and locked away where he could create no more waves.

In 1865, a small group of physicians led by Vienna's leading dermatologist, Ferdinand Ritter von Hebra (1816–80), lured Semmelweis to an asylum under the pretense that his opinion was sought on certain matters. As soon as Semmelweis was through the door he became suspicious and tried to leave, but von Hebra's henchmen were prepared and beat Semmelweis so badly that he died shortly after in one of the asylum's dungeons.

It is understandable that such entrenched and established opinion would be a large ship to turn, but when undisputable proof was clear for all to observe, it seems bizarre in the extreme that the only action the captains of that ship could think to take was to murder the messenger. But Semmelweis is not forgotten. In scientific circles, the "Semmelweis reflex" is a common expression used to describe the knee-jerk reaction of entrenched thinking to any suggestion that it might be wrong.

There is a missing link in the evolutionary chain.

The notion that there is a missing link in the evolutionary chain, an early human ancestor who would help explain the full transition from ape to man, was an accepted idea of both paleontology and anthropology until the early part of the twentieth century.

The descent of man: a smooth transition that bore little relation to reality

THE SEARCH BEGINS

Although the concept has no basis in scientific fact, the search for the missing link among the archaeological community has persisted since the late nineteenth century. While many have sought proof of such a link, others believed they had found it. A contingent of nineteenth-century anthropologists believed it still stalked the more remote regions of the planet—one demented soul even tried to breed it, with consequences that still ravage the Third World to this day.

The Dutch paleontologist Eugène Dubois (1858–1940) was the first to embark on a planned search for evidence of a missing link. In 1890 he was digging up half of Java, Indonesia, in his quest. In the latter part of that year he dug a pit near the Solo River in Eastern Java and unearthed the remains of what would become known as "Java Man," an admittedly simian-like creature that Dubois immediately pronounced to *be* the missing link. Few believed him, and he drew so much ire from academics that he gathered up the bones and became a virtual recluse. Dubois finally allowed full examination of Java Man in 1923, when it was quickly established that his find was nothing more than an example of *Homo erectus* (upright man). Dubois retreated into obscurity, never again to communicate with academia.

Not content with discovering mere remains of the so-called missing link, other individuals have supported the notion that the missing link has not died out but is still with us. We speak, of course, of Bigfoot—also known as Sasquatch, the yeti, or the abominable snowman.

Since the mid- to late nineteenth century the popular press has peddled the notion of Bigfoot as a living missing link. A rather surprising coterie of academic heavyweights have stood firmly in this corner, including Grover Krantz (1931–2002), professor of anthropology at Washington State University, and his colleague Geoffrey Bourne (1909–88), director of the internationally respected Yerkes National Primate Research Center in Atlanta, Georgia.

Such a notion was supported by John Napier (1917–87), an anthropologist, a primatologist, and a leading light at the Smithsonian Institute. The celebrity anthropologist Margaret Mead (1901–78) also believed that hairy missing

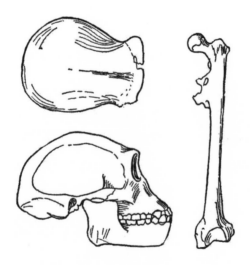

The remains of "Java Man"

links still stalked the snowlines—however, she also believed guardian aliens were sent here to observe us and ensure civilization was kept on the straight and narrow.

In 1953, the explorer Sir Edmund Hillary reported seeing yeti tracks and mounted an expedition in 1960 to gather evidence of the beast's existence. In 1959, actor James Stewart took possession of a supposed skeletonized yeti hand that had been stolen from Tibetan monks. Stewart smuggled it out of India to London for examination, where primatologist William Charles Osmond established that the hand was in fact Neanderthal. The anthropologist Jeffrey Meldrum (1958–), a professor at Idaho State University, actually went in search of Bigfoot in Siberia in 2011, though his expedition failed to yield any results.

REALITY CHECK
IT FELT LIKE A GOOD IDEA AT THE TIME

In the 1950s the World Health Organization (WHO) decided to combat Borneo's malaria problem by killing mosquitoes with DDT spray. Although a success, the spraying also killed off the wasps that fed on the roof-munching thatch-caterpillar, which promptly de-roofed the homes in the local area. Lots of cats also died after trying to lick themselves clean, which meant the rat-population exploded. The RAF then parachuted in more than 10,000 hungry felines to deal with the problem!

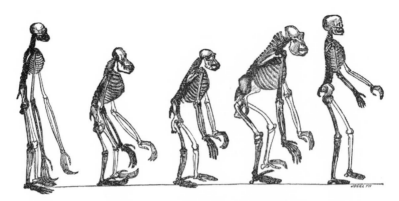

Different skeletons in profile
(from left to right): gibbon, orangutan,
chimpanzee, gorilla, and man

JUST ONE PROBLEM

The problem is these investigations had no basis in scientific fact: No one, Darwin included, has ever suggested that man is descended from apes. Had it been the case then there would be no apes left—they too would have evolved and would doubtless now be running banks or taking up seats in Congress. And despite nineteenth-century academia presenting the concept of man's descent in linear form, with clearly defined stages of development and advancement, this is now known to be very widely off the mark.

Desmond Morris's book *The Naked Ape* (1967), which sought to compare humans to other animals, is partially responsible for suggesting man descends from apes, as are the ever-popular posters that depict the evolution of man as a series of figures that become increasingly upright and devoid of body hair. What Darwin and others had proposed was that man and primate shared a common progenitor before dividing to descend in parallel, rather than in sequence.

The traditional perception of the descent of man as a sequential series of neat changes is completely inaccurate. The slow development followed a multi-branched and rather untidy path, with some branches dying out and others coexisting and even interbreeding across millennia. There were no cleanly divided stages.

REALITY CHECK
THE DESCENT OF DOG

Many species, including cats and dogs, were once the same species with common roots in the prehistoric genus *Miacis*, an arboreal dog-like creature with retractable claws used for climbing. This ancient progenitor lived around 50 million years ago, and since then it has subdivided by dictate of its diverse environments to produce cats, dogs, weasels, bears, and hyenas. Yet no sensible person would propose that dogs were descended from cats. It is also worth mentioning here that the hyena is the very confused marker of the cat–dog divide because, for all its appearance and countless references to it as a pack-hunting dog, the hyena is in fact more closely related to cats, evolutionarily speaking.

LENGTHY DIVERGENCE

In 2006, the exploration of the complex history of the human genome conducted by David Reich, a population geneticist at Harvard, revealed that the divergence of proto-humans and proto-chimpanzees from their common progenitor was a more lengthy and complicated process than previously thought. Just as late Neanderthals and early modern man cohabited and interbred (see box on facing page), so, too, did proto-humans and proto-chimpanzees over several million years. The recent tracking of the X chromosome in both modern man and chimpanzees reveals that the final divergence of the two species did not actually occur until between 5 and 6 million years ago, approximately 1 million years later than previously thought. But this still does not give support to the spurious theory of a missing link; it just means that early humans and chimpanzees remained similar enough in appearance to find one another acceptable breeding partners for longer than was previously assumed after they divided from the common progenitor.

THE IDEA WILL NOT DIE

Despite the fact there has never existed a tidy chain in our evolution from which a link could go missing, the idea itself will not get lost. Creationists, driven into a frenzy of denial by the publication of Darwin's *On the Origin of the Species*

MINI MYTH
NOT SO NEANDERTHAL

After the remains of a Neanderthal man were found in 1856 in the Neander Valley, just to the east of Düsseldorf, academics rushed to brand him a brutal, hunched, and hairy club-wielding humanoid. In reality, the Neanderthal was a far more civilized being.

Although slightly shorter and stockier than his modern counterpart, Neanderthal man was no troglodytic dolt. Possessing a brain approximately 3.4 ounces (100 milliliters) *larger* than his modern counterpart, Neanderthal man built individual and group dwellings and kept himself warm with fires. He cooked meat and vegetables, had his own language, and produced tools as sophisticated as those of co-evolving modern man, with whom Neanderthal man socially interacted and crossbred, as the present gene pool proves. (Approximately 4 percent of the DNA in Europeans and Asians is Neanderthal.)

As for the once held belief that "primitive" Neanderthals were driven to their rightful extinction by the rise of so-called modern man, this too has been quashed. Advances in DNA indicate that Neanderthal man was simply absorbed into early Cro-Magnon stock and modified through interbreeding. Neanderthal man, therefore, did not die out—he is still with us, a fact that will come as no surprise to female readers.

(1859), denounced him for allegedly suggesting that man was evolved from apes rather than created by God. As previously stated (see page 63), Darwin never suggested anything of the kind, but the press, among others, decided this was the thrust of his work, and those who had never read Darwin's seminal book were so keen to attack that they leapt on this ready-to-ride bandwagon.

By the advent of the 1900s, a British amateur archaeologist named Charles Dawson (1864–1916) was making a name for himself after he dug up half of Sussex to unearth some pretty interesting finds. In 1912, Dawson dramatically announced a staggering discovery: He had found the missing link—the skeletal remains of the long-sought ape-man—near the village of Piltdown, East Sussex.

It would be more than forty years before the "discovery" would be denounced as a fraud and the bones revealed to be the composite of a medieval human skull, the lower jaw of an orangutan, and chimpanzee teeth, all filed down to resemble a more human profile and appropriately aged in chemical solutions. But whether Dawson himself was the fraudster or had been unwittingly duped by another who had placed the find in his path has never been satisfactorily answered. It is, however, interesting to note that a near neighbor was Sir Arthur Conan Doyle, a man who was himself under heavy fire from the Christian Fundamentalists for his championing of the spiritualist movement. Not only was Doyle a resident of Piltdown, he was also, like

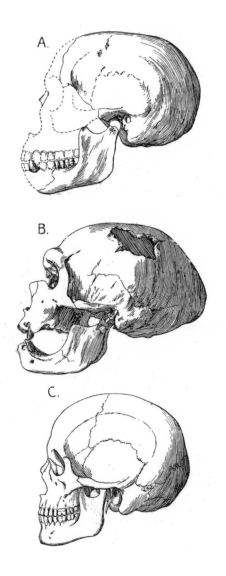

Compare and contrast:
(a) the Piltdown skull, (b) a Neanderthal skull,
and (c) a modern human skull

An artistic reconstruction of the Piltdown man

Dawson, a member of the Sussex Archaeological Society. The two would often be seen huddled together deep in conversation in the run-up to the "discovery."

In 1953, *Time* magazine published an article that completely debunked the so-called Piltdown Man, but by then the damage had been done—the idea of the missing link had etched itself irretrievably on to the public's consciousness.

In 1974, skeleton bones found in Ethiopia heralded a

further renaissance in the missing link theory. Known as "Lucy" (so named because the Beatles' "Lucy in the Sky in Diamonds" was playing on the geologists' tape deck as the first bones were unearthed), the skeleton did indeed present the image of a three-million-year-old chimpanzee-like creature that bore indications in the pelvic structure and knee joints of having walked upright. The discovery of an older and taller male version of Lucy in Ethiopia in 2010 lead to further excitement within some circles about the prospect of a missing link. But no one involved in either dig had at any point suggested the finds were anything of the sort.

STAGED INTERVENTION

Now on to the man who decided to produce his own missing link—Stalin's own Dr. Frankenstein, Soviet biologist Ilya Ivanovich Ivanov (1870–1932) and his Humanzee Project of the late 1920s. As early as 1910, Ivanov was openly musing the feasibility of creating a living, breathing missing link by crossbreeding humans with chimpanzees, orangutans, and even gorillas. Few doubted him; this, after all, was the man who had already produced a zeedonk (a zebra crossed with a donkey) and crossbred or cross-inseminated a range of animals from cows with antelopes to rabbits with rats.

By 1925 Ivanov had secured Humanzee funding from

the Kremlin and, rightly thinking such experiments to be better conducted as far away from Moscow as possible, he and his son, also called Ilya, headed for the less stringently controlled environs of Africa. On a more sinister note, Ivanov considered Africa best suited for his program because, as "everybody knew," Africans are closer to our simian forebears than are white Europeans, and he was going to need human participants in his grotesque fiasco.

The summer of 1926 saw the Ivanovs ensconced in the city of Conakry, in what was then French New Guinea. But exactly what happened next is unclear. It is known that the first round of experiments centered on inseminating female chimpanzees with human sperm. However the methodology involved has been the subject of lurid speculation. Ivanov always refused to discuss his methods beyond stating that the donors had all been African men who had been "well paid for their input"—an unfortunate term given the nature of all contemporary and subsequent speculation.

The second round of experiments centered on African women inseminated with sperm donations from chimpanzees. But, again, just how many times this was tried and failed is unclear. By 1927 the French were disturbed by the unsettling rumors that had begun to circulate, and they obliged the Ivanovs to return to Russia, where they were given facilities in Sukhumi in Stalin's native Georgia. However, none of their experiments bore any results, and, in the time-honored tradition of Stalin's regime, the elder Ivanov was rewarded with a one-way ticket to exile, where he died a couple of years later.

REALITY CHECK
HALF-MAN–HALF-APE ARMY

Although there is no evidence that Ivanov knew of the Kremlin's motive for funding his bizarre set of experiments, it has since come to light that Stalin and Lavrentiy Beria, his secret-police chief, were keen to see if it would be possible to breed a whole new half-man–half-ape army. When not laboring uncomplainingly to harvest the country's resources in the inhospitable north, they would make ideal soldiers because chimps are instinctively tribal and much given to organized war in their natural environment. This, coupled with their ability to outrun Olympic sprinters and single-handedly pull up to 1,000 pounds on a torque bar, would have made Humanzees a fearsomely brutish and perhaps mindlessly obedient force. At least, that was what Stalin and Beria had hoped for.

DEVASTATING CONSEQUENCES

But the fallout from his folly may still be with us. Although HIV and AIDS was, until recently, thought by most to be a disease of the 1980s, it is now clear that SIV, the simian equivalent, somehow jumped the species barrier to become HIV some time in the late 1920s, with Guinea being a leading location for instances of infection.

When HIV was first identified as a variant of SIV, rumors abound that the barrier had been breached by human–monkey sexual activity in the jungle. More conservative medical opinion suggested careless handling of bushmeat kills by hunters was responsible. But hunters in Africa have been hunting and butchering chimpanzees and other Old World monkeys for thousands of years, so why would it have taken so long for SIV to make the jump?

In the recent past, medical opinion has been reappraised and is looking again at the HIV implications of the experiments of Ivanov and those of his equally misguided Russian contemporary, Serge Voronoff (see page 59).

BACK TO THE BEGINNING

One final word on the descent of man: For some time now, Africa has been regarded as the cradle of modern humanity. This notion moved from academic circles into the public consciousness in 2001 with the publication of Bryan Sykes's intriguing work of nonfiction *The Seven Daughters of Eve*. Sykes estimated that the first real human beings emerged in Central and Eastern Africa approximately 200,000 years ago.

But anthropologists will keep digging. In 2006, human teeth and countless animal bones bearing distinctive marks that indicate flesh had been stripped from them with flint implements were found in the Qesem Caves of Rosh Ha'Ayin, Israel. The remains were dated 200,000 years earlier than any African find. So unless Africa can come up with an earlier bid, the Holy Land holds the chalice—for the time being, at least.

African and Polynesian societies indulged in cannibalism.

The concept of cannibalism, that man could commit perhaps the ultimate crime of eating a fellow human being, has fascinated civilizations since ancient times. Hindu and Greek mythologies teem with examples of gods eating their own children, or vengeful wives serving up a favorite son in a stew to the unwitting and doting father. Today, people still tell the focus of their desires that they could eat them up, and there are numerous other edible metaphors for sex.

PAPAL TYRANNY

There was also in ancient times the well-established trend that required the devoted to sacrifice and devour a proxy for whichever god or demigod they worshiped. However, these would have been individual acts of anthrophagy (the eating of human flesh) conducted in a respectful and almost reverential way: the ingestion of blood and select body parts, such as the heart. Usually this was done to ensure the passage to heaven, or even rebirth, of the consumed. Although such concepts now seem primitive, today's Christians routinely partake in metaphorical anthrophagy: The wine-and-wafer ceremony of the Mass or Communion is thought to represent "the blood and body of Christ."

While there is a well-established history of such individual acts in ancient times, there has also existed a long-standing belief in the existence of countless African and Polynesian societies that indulged in routine anthrophagy as a staple part of their diet. Not challenged until the late twentieth century, this broadly accepted anthropological "truth" formed the basis of many expeditions that were usually followed by a highly lucrative lecture tour that brought the concept into the public awareness. Even today, no film of the *Indiana Jones* or *Lost World* genre is complete without at least one scene of someone being dropped into a pot on a low heat with suitably gruesome and bone-bedecked savages dancing around their dinner-to-be. And who is responsible for the spread of such ideas? The fifteenth-century Vatican and its avaricious rush to lay claim to the rest of the world.

THE AGE OF EXPLOITATION

During the Age of Exploration, from the fifteenth to the seventeenth centuries, the Catholic countries of Spain and Portugal stood at the helm of the discovery of the New World.

An illustration of the landing of Columbus

In addition to the gold and silver mined in these new lands, the profits to be made from slavery were enormous. Understandably, the Vatican felt in need of a veneer of justification for this slave trade, which itself presented a problem. Numerous popes and cardinals owned slaves, and the galleys of the papal navy ran on chained labor. But although the Bible abounded with divine justification of slavery of every kind, the Vatican was not anxious to make this known to the populations of Europe at large.

It must be remembered that this was a time when the Good Book was available only in Latin and any non-cleric who so much as peeked inside its covers could be burned alive for their curiosity. Anthrophagy, it seemed, presented the ideal solution. No indigenous peoples of new lands could be enslaved—we are all God's children, after all— unless they were found to be man-eaters, in which case they were not God's children but to be held lower than the beasts of the fields over which the Lord had given man do- minion. Therefore man must have dominion over beings that ranked below beasts.

CANNIBALISM IS BORN

Before unleashing the rapacious Columbus on the unsus- pecting peoples of foreign lands, Spain's Queen Isabella I of Castile and her husband, Ferdinand II of Aragon, sought clarification on the matter from Pope Alexander VI, a man not unaccustomed to employing a little brute force (see page 81). He was only too pleased to clarify, construct- ing the notorious Demarcation Line down the map of the world, with the Spanish to be kept to the west of it, and Portuguese to the east.

In 1492, Columbus duly headed for the Americas. Upon his arrival in the Caribbean, Columbus cynically pronounced the indigenous Canniba people to be wanton man-eaters and diligently set about their slaughter or enslavement. As this was the first major exercise of such a nature, the unfortunate natives' name gave rise to the term cannibal. Naturally, as soon as the explorers made landfall on a new country, they pronounced the entire population to be man-eaters and broke out the manacles, or worse. On Haiti alone, the Spanish reduced the indigenous Taino population from 500,000 to 350 people in a mere thirty years.

An artistic representation of Columbus's landing from a book dated 1891

*An early representation of
South American natives*

To justify their preposterous claims, the enslaving expeditions published lurid pamphlets on their return, complete with etchings of trussed captives looking glum in their
cooking pots. These pamphlets would become standard
reference material for the early anthropologists of the eighteenth and nineteenth centuries, who set out in search of
suitably terrifying tribes. But their quests never quite came
to fruition—no single anthropologist ever visited a village
in which the occupants acknowledged themselves to be
cannibals.

THINGS DON'T ADD UP

It is extraordinary that these early anthropologists failed to ask basic questions that would have revealed the truth behind the fiction. How, for example, did Stone Age African or Polynesian tribesmen possess iron pots big enough to cook up the meat harvested from three or four victims? They also failed to work out the math: These were people who led an extremely harsh and active life without the comfort of an abundance of food. The average lithe native would produce up to ten pounds of meat at best, which would leave a village of one hundred adults requiring about ten victims for one decent meal. In the space of one year, the occupants of that one cannibalistic village would eat their way through something in the region of 4,000 of their neighbors—hardly a realistic prospect, given the population levels of such areas.

Anthropologists also failed to address the issues of practicality: The animals of the forests and the fishes of the rivers would have contributed a much higher meat yield, and they would not have shot back. Medical implications involved in eating one's fellow man would also have taken their toll. Eating humans is not good for you. Humans carry a dangerous prion, a protein particle thought to cause brain disease, similar to that which causes CJD, or "mad cow disease." The Fore tribe of Papua New Guinea, one of the few tribes known to conduct funeral cannibalistic rites, nearly wiped itself out in the late 1950s with a fatal condition similar to CJD, known locally as *kuru*, or the shaking death.

Anthropologists have certainly found ancient human bones bearing marks they claim were caused by butchery, but they cannot know the circumstances in which these injuries occurred. Starvation cannibalism is far from unknown in the apparently civilized West. The first English settlers of Jamestown, Virginia, resorted to eating one another when food supplies ran out in 1609; the Russians dined on one another in the Siege of Leningrad during World War II; and the diet of those who survived the Andean plane crash of 1972 is now common knowledge. Indeed, the vast majority of authenticated acts of cannibalism have involved white Europeans.

A PECKISH PACKER

The first prosecution for starvation cannibalism occurred in nineteenth-century America with the celebrated case of Alfred "Alferd" Packer (1842–1907). In November 1873, Packer foolishly led a party of gold prospectors from Gunnison, Colorado, up into the high country where, predictably, the weather trapped them in their shack. Packer soon realized that the only food he was going to find before the thaw set in would have to be provided, quite literally, by his clients. When Packer returned to Gunnison looking surprisingly well fed considering his ordeal, questions were asked . . . and the answers turned everyone pale.

Packer's subsequent trial is famous in America, not least for the presiding judge's summation. Judge Melville B. Gerry, a Democratic in the predominantly Republican state of Colorado, clearly felt a personal grudge against the defendant. Ordering Packer to stand for sentencing, Gerry said, "Damn you, Packer, there were only seven Democrats in the whole of Hinsdale County and you, you low-down son-of-a-bitch, ate five of them!"

The Earth is a hollow vessel.

Early religion touted the notion of a hollow Earth, a vessel that housed the "land of final punishment" for anyone who failed to conduct themselves in accordance with an individual religion's various dictates. For the Ancient Greeks hollow Earth was the Underworld, ruled by the god Hades, where all people, good or bad, ended up. For the Christians it was, and still is, the place we call Hell.

SCIENCE GETS INVOLVED

Inspired by theological pronouncements of an underground world, early science took the theory to heart and explored the concept. According to the proponents of the hollow Earth theory, our planet possessed a variety of characteristics, including an interior sun at its core, a living population, and access points at the Poles or in Tibet. Opinions on the exact details of the hollow Earth's makeup differed according to the sources.

In 1692, Edmond Halley (1656–1742), the astronomer and polymath of comet fame, advanced a theory that suggested the planet was a hollow shell that contained three inner shells. He believed each independent and inhabited sphere was separated from its neighboring sphere by its own atmosphere. The access points to the interior of the earth were, according to Halley, located at the Poles, and gases escaping from within the earth manifested themselves as the aurora borealis. Halley's hypothesis drew considerable recognition.

It was Halley's 1676 voyage to St. Helena to observe the star constellations in the southern hemisphere that started him thinking seriously about the ancient hollow Earth theory. He was struck by the inconsistencies in his compass

REALITY CHECK
TURNING UP THE HEAT

Mark Twain once remarked, "Heaven for the climate, but Hell for the company" but, according to the Bible, Heaven is the hotter of the two. Isaiah 30:26 describes that in Heaven "the light of the sun shall be sevenfold as the light of seven days," which, according to a series of weighty calculations involving the Stefan–Boltzmann fourth power law of radiation, gives us a temperature of 977° Fahrenheit (525° Celsius). Hell, the Bible tells us, abounds with pits of liquid brimstone (sulfur), so the temperature there must be 833° Fahrenheit (445 degrees Celsius), because any temperature higher than that turns sulfur into gas.

The hollow earth with access points at both Poles

readings, which seemed to vary even on the same spot on consecutive days. What else could account for this except another rotating sphere, or two, within the casing of the planet? Of course, what Halley did not then know was that this discrepancy in compass readings is quite normal: The lines of the Earth's magnetic field do not run in straight lines between the Poles, but in a series of erratic lines, which themselves shift.

The idea that the lines of the Earth's magnetic field were caused by something deep within the Earth was the thrust of the first part of Halley's 1692 submission to the Royal Society. If one allowed for the notion of other spheres that possessed their own magnetic fields, which rotate at different speeds or even in different directions, then this would account for the varying compass readings. Halley informed the assembled members of the Royal Society that

---

REALITY CHECK
The Unreliable Compass

The old-fashioned needle compass aligns itself with whichever line is nearest and thus never points to true North, unless by pure coincidence. The lines are generated by the rotating, solid iron ball at the center of the planet, which is, at present, behaving in a rather worrying way. Things, it seems, are afoot beneath our feet, and some feel the Earth is preparing for a reversal of its own polarization. This change happens approximately every 250,000 years, and we are long overdue such an upheaval.

---

his notions fitted with the theological perspective that the Almighty would not, in His wisdom, have created the massive bulk of the world "simply to support its surface" but instead "to yield as great a surface as possible for the use of living creatures as can consist with the convenience and security of the whole." When asked why the oceans did not drain away into the hollow after sub-oceanic earthquakes tore open cracks in the Earth's surface, Halley's answer was that the outer sphere, perhaps 500 miles thick, was obviously self-healing due to the presence of "saline and vitriolic particles as may contribute to petrification."

Halley concluded his submission by saying that "The concave arches may in several places shine with such a substance as invests the surface of the Sun and I have adventured to make these subterranean orbs capable of being inhabited." From those last few words on the subject there sprang a whole new interest in hollow-earthism.

DEARLY DEVOTED

The list of those who took Halley at his tantalizing word is long to say the least, but among the more prominent were the Norwegian-born essayist and philosopher Ludvig Holberg (1684–1754), who enshrined his ideas in the novel *The Journey of Niels Klim to the World Underground* (1741). In a yarn that would long predate Jules Verne's altogether more enjoyable *Journey to the Center of the Earth* (1863), Holberg's fantasy tells the story of a young student who discovers a series of worlds within our own after falling into a cave. His exciting journey leads him to explore new lands and strange creatures that live under the earth's crust.

The eighteenth-century hollow-earthers also counted among its ranks the Scottish mathematician and physicist Sir John Leslie (1776–1832). In his *Elements of Natural Philosophy* (1829) he devotes nearly half a dozen pages to the concept. In the nineteenth century the leading lights of the lobby were the Americans John Cleves Symmes (1779–1829), James McBride (1788–1859), and Jeremiah Reynolds (1799–1858). The first is best described as a well-connected adventurer, McBride was a leading light of Miami University, and

Reynolds a well-respected newspaper editor and explorer.

Together the three men lobbied President John Quincy Adams (1767–1848), who, as a proponent of the hollow Earth theory, agreed to fund from the public purse an expedition to the South Pole to find the portal to the supposed subterranean wonders. However, the project was abandoned when Adams's replacement, the altogether more hard-headed Andrew Jackson (1767–1845), threw the idea and its proponents out on their collective ear.

Undeterred, Reynolds immediately raised funds for the expedition from private backers and speculators, and set sail in late 1929 in search of his goal. His crew, however, were unconvinced, and having quickly tired of looking for a big hole in the earth's surface under the supervision of a man they thought was crazy, they mutinied and set Reynolds ashore on the coast of Chile before sailing off in his ship. Reynolds was forced to wait in Valparaiso until 1932, when he was eventually rescued by an American ship.

NAZI INVOLVEMENT

Not one to let a dubious scientific theory pass by unnoticed, Adolf Hitler too propagated the theory of a hollow Earth. The Thule Society, a large collection of right-wing eccentrics who adhered to all sorts of mystical notions, provided the hub of support in Germany. It was from this semi-clandestine society that the Nazi Party itself sprang. The Thulians believed the access to the inner world lay in Tibet, a country they also believed to be the cradle of a long-lost master race—Hitler and a majority of his henchmen also believed this to be true.

In 1938, Hitler and Heinrich Himmler sent an expedition to Tibet to find anthropological evidence of the supposed master race and, while they were there, to investigate any suspiciously large holes they might happen to encounter. The expedition heard much talk of the fabled underworld cities of Agartha and Shambhala (now known as "Shangri-La" to Westerners) and the superior beings who lived there. Despite the explorers leaving their first expedition empty-handed, Hitler had not yet finished with the Underworld. In 1943 the Führer decided it was time he explored the other hollow earth theory: the earth is a concave sphere and all living creatures inhabit its inside surface.

In April 1942, Hitler sent an expedition under the leadership of Dr. Heinz Fischer to Rügen Island, located in the Baltic Sea, where they set up camp with powerful telescopes and radar. They were under instruction to aim their instruments up at the sky, rather than across the sea, to spy on Allied activity on the other side of the world. Unsurprisingly, the members of the expedition returned to Berlin in late May empty-handed and no doubt fearful of reprisal from their dogmatic leader. Fortunately for them, the high-ranking Nazi Reinhard Heydrich had recently been assassinated in Czechoslovakia, and Hitler was far more interested in plotting his revenge. Relieved, Fischer took himself off to secure obscurity and all further Nazi-led hollow Earth projects were abandoned. But the theory of a hollow Earth did not die out with Hitler. There remain today countless hollow Earth societies, all of which, of course, believe that the successes of the various NASA-led space programs are but a charade to keep us from communicating with our inner selves.

The bodies of animals contain a life energy that can be influenced by external magnetic forces.

To suggest someone possesses an animal magnetism is to imply they are sexually attractive or have a charismatic allure, but the original meaning of the expression suggested nothing of the kind. First realized in the eighteenth century, animal magnetism was a new "science" that suggested people and animals possessed a universal fluid that could be influenced by an external magnetic force. This notion held sway for some considerable time, and would go on to spawn the phenomenon of hypnotism.

ANIMAL MAGNETISM

Austrian-born Franz Anton Mesmer (1734–1815), a physician with an interest in astronomy, first devised the concept of animal magnetism, and he did so under the tutelage of the incongruously named Jesuit astronomer Father Maximilian Hell (1720–92).

Aside from his interest in the universe, Maximilian Hell also had a keen interest in the spurious field of magnetic therapy, born in part from his familiarity with the Chinese concept of qi (pronounced "chee"). This notion centered on the ancient oriental belief that certain vital energies flow through the body and that the disruption of these energies can lead to bad health. Wellness is reestablished by redirecting the flow of qi using a variety of techniques, from feng shui to acupuncture and magnet therapy.

The acupuncture needles and magnets were intended to act like corporeal traffic police by redirecting the energy flow to its correct route. Hell had no time for acupuncture; he was convinced the magnets, rather than the needles, held the key to the cure. Hell started to build medicinal magnet theory into his lectures, and his student Mesmer joined him wholeheartedly in his folly.

Mesmer was also greatly influenced by the British royal physician Richard Mead (1673–1754), the "Father of Foundlings," whose spacious residence in Bloomsbury, London, would form the foundation of the Great Ormond Street Hospital for Sick Children. Mead had a keen interest in astronomy and—after his close friend Isaac Newton discovered the universal force of gravity—postulated that just as the planets exerted a gravitational pull on the Earth, they similarly influenced the flow of fluids within animals and humans.

While the gravitational pull of the moon creates tides in the Earth's oceans, for example, the human body is far too small an object to be subjected to similar effects. Mesmer, however, used the false postulations of Hell and Mead to devise the concept of animal gravitation.

Mesmer next observed the Bavarian priest exorcist Johann Gassner (1727–79) during a routine exorcism. Mesmer concluded that the patient's possession was alleviated by the magnetism that emitted from a metal cross the priest had used to beat and stroke the afflicted. In the belief that there might be an interaction between a natural magnetic quality within the body and the external magnetic force, Mesmer devised the concept of animal magnetism.

Mesmer was convinced that a universal fluid, a force that flowed like liquid through all living creatures, could be manipulated by an external magnetic influence. In order to test his hypothesis, Mesmer subjected his patients to a variety of bizarre treatments, one of which included having them sit in a vat of diluted sulfuric acid while they held on to iron bars that carried a low-voltage current.

MESMERISM

By 1775 Mesmer abandoned the use of magnets and electricity altogether, as he had become convinced that he himself was the vector directing and controlling the ebb and flow of a person's universal fluid. By this stage his patients

REALITY CHECK
THE INFLUENCE OF THE MOON

Planetary influence on the well-being of humankind was not in itself a new notion. The word *lunatic*, derived from the Latin *luna* (moon), suggested the full moon could induce abnormal behavior in those who were normally sane. In the days before street lighting there may have been some foundation in such a notion. Taking advantage of the free light provided by the full moon, people might well have stayed out longer, allowing them the opportunity to drink more than usual. Or perhaps they always behaved like that and it was just that their transgressions were more visible to sober observers.

were required to sit in mesmeric cubicles, which, they were told, would concentrate "the force" on them.

Nor was Mesmer alone in his beliefs—many physicians of significant standing followed his teachings, and "mesmerism" became popular throughout eighteenth-century Europe. In Mesmer's defense, his research did lead to a groundbreaking discovery; unfortunately he was too enamored with the notion of animal magnetism to acknowledge the phenomenon for what it really was.

Mesmer enjoyed some considerable success in his sessions, which had become a cross between a pseudoscience and spiritual healing. His success, however, may have been

Franz Anton Mesmer at work

the result of his propensity to focus his attentions on hypochondriacs, hysterics, and those otherwise susceptible to his suggestions. The most celebrated of such patients was the talented pianist Maria Theresia von Paradis (1759–1824), whose father was prominent in the Austrian court and held the ear of the Empress Maria Theresa, after whom he had named his daughter.

Having suffered from "hysterical blindness" since the age of four, the eighteen-year-old Maria Theresia experienced a temporary improvement in her sight under the guidance of Mesmer. But when it was suggested that Mesmer had used his influence over Maria Theresia to put her into one of his famous mesmeric trances for other, less salubrious purposes, her parents felt they had no option but to dispense with his services. As soon as the treatments were terminated the blindness returned and remained with Maria Theresia for the rest of her life.

This illustration adorns the frontispiece of
Confessions of a Magnetizer,
an 1845 exposé of animal magnetism.

The whiff of scandal was enough to force Mesmer to quit Vienna and head to Paris, where he continued his lucrative practice. Mesmer began to record that the influence he communicated to his patients induced what he called a magnetic trance, or magnetic somnambulance. Although he did not realize it, Mesmer was hypnotizing his patients.

MESMER IS MARGINALIZED

As Mesmer's bandwagon picked up momentum in France, Louis XVI came under increasing pressure to establish a scientific inquiry into the matter. Despite being one of Mesmer's patients, Louis XVI finally gave the green light in 1784 for a Commission. One of the members of the committee was Dr. Joseph-Ignace Guillotin, an expert in pain management whose name would soon be made infamous by the impending French Revolution.

Guillotin and his cocommittee members found no merit in Mesmer's methods or treatments, and they denounced him as a fraud. Another prominent name on the committee, Benjamin Franklin (1706–90), one of the Founding Fathers of the United States, then in Paris as the United States Minister to France, concurred, although he did add that Mesmer clearly had an idea of the role the mind played in sickness and its cure.

HYPNOTIC

As Mesmer became increasingly marginalized, one of his French students, José Faria (1746–1819), an Indo-Portuguese monk from Goa, began to incorporate the techniques used in oriental hypnotism into the sessions. The results were revelatory. Finally realizing that hypnotism, and not animal magnetism, lay at the heart of Mesmer's sessions, Faria pronounced that "Nothing comes from the magnetizer: everything comes from the subject and takes place in his imagination; [it is] autosuggestion generated from within the mind [of the subject]."

Faria's take on the matter would outlive him. His methods were later observed by the English physician James Braid (1795–1860), who in 1841 made a close study of this modified form of mesmerism and refined it to become the first modern clinical hypnotism, a term he coined himself.

With this new life breathed into the phenomenon of mesmerism, others sought to apply the concept to the rest of the animal kingdom. The methods employed by North African and Indian snake charmers were reevaluated—was it just a street trick, or did something more sophisticated occur between the charmer and the charmed? Chickens, too, seemed to fall into a trance if held down against the ground as a chalk line was drawn away from the tip of their beak.

Unfortunately for those who like to believe in such things, animals cannot be mesmerized or hypnotized. The snake-charming acts are nothing but a street trick; the music from the charmer's flute is quite unnecessary to the ruse, as its pitch lies outside of a snake's auditory range. (It is a myth too that snakes are deaf—they simply do not have external ears, only internal ones that pick up vibration

A chicken undergoing hypnosis

through the ground.) The key to the trick is the tapping of the charmer's foot and the movement of his flute.

The strike distance of a cobra is approximately two-thirds of its body length, and the creature has motion-sensitive vision. The foundation to a long career as a snake charmer lies in their ability to position themselves just outside of that range, but not so far that the snake loses interest and slides back down into its basket. The snake appears to mimic the flute's movement from side to side, as if in a trance; in reality it is preparing itself to strike the charmer, should the opportunity present itself.

Chickens, on the other hand, go into a state of thanatosis (feigned death), in response to the sheer fear they experience at being held immobile, as if in the grip of a predator. The carefully drawn chalk line is a mere piece of theatre, unnecessary to the procedure.

THE LEGACY LIVES ON

While mesmerism finally waned, and its offspring, hypnotism, went on to achieve greater things, certain charlatans were not yet done with magnet therapy. There still exists today a multimillion-dollar industry that peddles magnetic bangles to the gullible, promising improved blood flow and relief from pain in the wrists and hands. An Internet search for "magnetic bracelets" renders nearly 2 million sites.

Nor has Mesmer's original idea of a universal force

that flows through the bodies of all animals been completely disregarded. For some, *orgone*, a so-called cosmic energy discovered by the Austrian-born psychiatrist and psychoanalyst Wilhelm Reich (1897–1957), held the key. For others it was, and still is for some, *vril*, a powerful life-giving and life-destroying force first introduced in Edward Bulwer-Lytton's 1871 novel *The Coming Race*, which some took to be a fictionalized realization of a very real force. Mesmer's ideas even form the foundation of the Star Wars franchise, in which the Force is always with those willing to recognize and harness it.

A close friend of Sigmund Freud and a member of the so-called Vienna Circle, Reich was captivated by Freud's notion of libido. For Reich libido was the universal force, which he chose to call *orgone* (a blend of *orgasm* and *ozone*). Under the pretense that he could tap into the vibrations of an enduring cosmic orgasm, Reich built orgone accumulators, largely modeled on the mesmeric cubicles and into which he invited his human guinea pigs for a quick blast of celestial sex-energy. Reich's accumulator was essentially a Faraday cage (invented in 1836 by the English scientist Michael Faraday for the use in blocking external electric fields), insulated on the outside by wood and lined on the inside with thin steel sheeting. He believed the orgone accumulator contained concentrated orgone energy that could be used to cure illness in those who were experiencing an imbalance in their orgone.

Participants emerged claiming to feel suitably invigo-
rated, however Reich did select his volunteers from a circle
of the already converted. Interestingly, Reich did attract
some notable names to his camp—even Albert Einstein
(1879–1955) thought there might be something in it. After
a five-hour meeting between the two men at Princeton University in January 1941, Einstein declared that if Reich's
experiments revealed a detectable rise in temperature in
one of his accumulators without a known heat source, then
the basic laws of physics would have been discredited.

Reich returned to Princeton with an accumulator so Einstein could observe for himself the increase in temperature.
And observe it he did. Einstein's experiments revealed a
noticeable increase in the internal temperature of the accumulator; however, this increase was detectable only in
the upper section of the box, and it was soon established
the temperature change was the consequence of convection
currents from the room itself and not the result of a cosmic
influence.

The accumulators were not airtight; the only thing they
did accumulate was warm air from without. In 1954 the US
Food and Drug Administration (FDA) issued Reich with
an injunction, banning him from selling or transporting his
accumulators. But Reich was by then a psychotic paranoid
with delusions of grandeur, and he chose to ignore the writ.
He ended his days in a psychiatric prison, a somewhat dis-
graced figure. Reich's accumulators are still available to

MINI MYTHS
WELL, I NEVER!
POPULAR SCIENTIFIC IDEAS DEBUNKED

- Water does not spiral down the drain in different directions in the northern and southern hemispheres.

- Goldfish have pretty good memories and can even be taught a trick or two!

- Black holes do not absorb surrounding matter.

- Electricity actually flows from negative to positive.

- The Big Bang Theory relates to the early evolution of the universe, not its inception.

buy online for a mere $5,000, which the unkind might say is a touch steep for what is essentially a steel-lined coffin. But many are willing to pay such sums to be at one with the universe.

THE NEXT GENERATION

Bulwer-Lytton's vril was perhaps mesmerism's most sinister spin-off. *The Coming Race* combined the notion of a hollow Earth (see page 147) with the universal force of mesmerism. For Bulwer-Lytton, vril flowed like a magical fluid through the bodies of a subterranean superrace that was biding its time for a terrestrial takeover. Such was the international popularity of this yarn it even inspired product names such as Bovril—a blend of *bovine* and *vril*.

The Coming Race was a great hit in Germany, especially among certain societies that had started to emerge in the early 1900s. The Thule Society in particular thought the book was fact masquerading as fiction. The Thulians believed the Earth was a hollow vessel, within which dwelled the mythical Aryan race, biding its time before bursting forth on to the Earth's surface to take over the world.

From the Thulian membership would emerge the Nazi Party (see page 152). Under the guiding hand of Himmler, in 1935 Hitler set up the *Studiengesellschaft für Geistergeschichte, Deutsches Ahnenerbe* (the Study Society for Spiritual History and German Ancestral Heritage), which was charged with proving the existence of a subterranean superrace. Their mission was to establish contact and reassure the subterranean dwellers that they had allies on the surface who would be there to support them when the time came.

This was the hidden agendum of the infamous 1938 German expedition to Tibet, as led by SS member and German hunter Ernst Schäfer (1910–92) and his Deputy Expedition Leader, fellow SS member Bruno Berger (1911–2009). The official reason given for the expedition was to research the geography and culture of the region, but Berger and his SS colleagues did little more than take cranial measurements of the local people and make phrenological head casts with the results.

The last word on the subject of animal magnetism is awarded to Willy Ley (1906–69), the leading rocket scientist who had the good sense to leave Germany in 1935. In 1947 Ley wrote an article called "Pseudoscience in Naziland" in which he mentioned a sub-group of the Thule Society that was exclusively founded on the contents of Bulwer-Lytton's *The Coming Race*.

"The next group was literally founded upon a novel," wrote Ley. "That group, which I think called itself *Wahrheitsgesellschaft* (the Society for Truth) and which was more or less localized in Berlin, devoted its spare time looking for vril." Indeed there still exist vril societies throughout Europe and North America today. Perhaps someone should tell them it was all just a story.

The body is made up of four humors—blood, phlegm, yellow bile, and black bile.

From Ancient Greece to the mid- to late nineteenth century, the "humor theory"—the idea that the body is made up of four main fluids—was a broadly accepted phenomenon.

Consisting of blood, phlegm, yellow bile, and black bile, an imbalance in the four humors was said to cause all sickness and mental malaise. Too much phlegm and a person would become phlegmatic; an excess of blood (or *sanguis*) was thought to make a person sanguine; too much yellow bile (or *chole*) would likely induce cholera; and too much black bile (or *melanchole*) and a person would sink into a melancholy mood. These four basic concepts constituted a comprehensive framework of health and disease made available to doctors until it was superseded by scientific medicine in the nineteenth century.

This engraving dates from the sixteenth century and shows the perceived balance of the four humors

FOUNDATION STONES

The foundation for the humor theory lay in Hippocratic medicine. Beginning with the Ancient Greek medic Hippocrates (c. 460–c. 370 BCE) and developed by unknown individuals over the course of next two centuries, the Hippocratic Corpus was later introduced to the West by the physician, surgeon, and pivotal figure in Greek medicine Galen (129–c. 210 CE). The theory held that each of the four humors was identified with a body part and linked to one of the four elements—phlegm was matched with the brain and water, blood with the heart and air, black bile with the spleen and the Earth, and yellow bile with the liver and fire. The properties of the four humors were heat, cold, dryness, and moistness.

The Hippocratic approach was holistic—the ancient Greeks knew little about the human anatomy, as they were averse to dissecting human bodies; they favored instead a surface inspection of their patients to see if they could spot the likely signs of disease. Physicians believed they could read the complex balance of the four humors in an individual's face, hence *complexion*. The cosmetics trade was in part put into hyperdrive by the humor theory, as both men and women tried to present to the world a visage that spoke well of their physical and mental disposition. The multibillion-dollar industry thus has the Greeks to thank for its existence. As the theory expanded, it embraced the notion that you are what you eat. Foods were categorized according to the effect they had on the humors, and this shaped the different cooking styles of medieval Europe.

MINI MYTH
FOOD, GLORIOUS FOOD

The different nations of medieval Europe each had a slightly different take on how food might influence a person's humoral balance. Red meat was thought to anger the blood, but if cooked in honey the effect would be reduced. An imbalance in bile could be treated with foods dressed in saffron. Not only did the humor theory invade the medieval kitchen, the chefs themselves rose to physician-like status, commanding considerable pay and respect.

BLOODY EXCESS

Proponents of the four humors believed the body could heal itself, and their procedures were designed to encourage the body in this natural healing process by purging it of its bad humors. Bloodletting was a common practice, often carried out to help alleviate fever and to remove excess blood, and it continued well into the mid-nineteenth century. So popular was bloodletting that, no matter their condition, many patients were bled relentlessly by their doctors, often with terminal results. President George Washington (1731–99), British poet Lord Byron (1788–1824), and the Scottish poet and playwright Sir Walter

Scott (1771–1832) all died as a result of bloodletting by well-intentioned doctors.

The notion that humoral bleeding improved a person's outlook was so popular that even barbers would help patients dispense with a pint or two. In the fourteenth century the Worshipful Company of Barbers and Surgeons was established to enable barbers to come to the aid of monks, who

There will be blood: a lithograph from 1804

> ## MINI MYTH
> ### LINGUISTIC LEGACY
>
> Adherents to the humor theory thought the liver, and not the heart, was the seat of courage. The heart was believed to be the home of learning, hence to "learn something by heart." The liver was thought to house a reservoir of yellow bile, which supposedly deserted the organ in times of stress, hence the cowardly are sometimes said to be either "lily livered" or "yellow bellied."

at that time were the official practitioners of medicine but who were banned from spilling blood by papal decree. The company was eventually dissolved in 1745 when the surgeons broke away to form the Company of Surgeons, yet its legacy can still be seen in the barber's pole today: The brass cap represents the collection bowl, and the red-and-white stripes the blood seeping through the bandaged incision.

FOUNDATION STONE

Hippocratic medicine highlighted the role the brain played in influencing a person's emotions, an idea previously unfamiliar within Ancient Greece, where it was believed the heart was responsible for a person's mental functions. Humorists believed mental health was dictated by the humoral

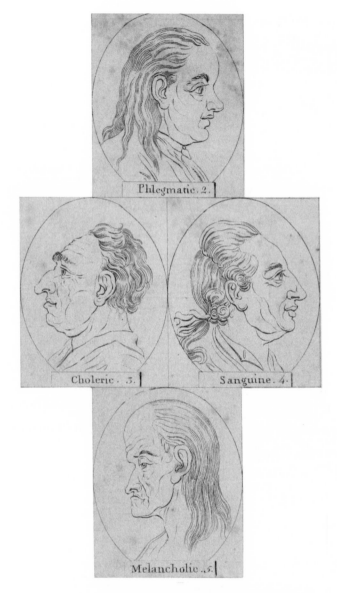

*A look says it all: the faces of the four humors.
(Clockwise from top) phlegmatic, sanguine,
melancholic, and choleric*

balance, which provided the foundations for modern psychology. To *temper* something is to mix or blend, and the right blend of the humors was believed to engender a good *temperament*. To the proto-psychologist there were four main temperaments, each dictated by the four cardinal humors. The sanguine were believed to be impulsive and extroverted yet also lofty and prone to taking delight in being hurtful to those near to them. The choleric were aggressive control freaks who did well in the world of politics. The phlegmatic were passive-aggressive types who made good followers. And the melancholic, well, they spoke for themselves. While these beliefs were very broad, this was the start of a scientific understanding of what went on in the minds of those in a distracted or depressed state.

The alternative practice of homeopathy also has its roots in the humor theory. Distressed at the bloodletting, leeching, purging, and other undignified and potentially terminal procedures that were being carried out, the German-born physician Christian Samuel Friedrich Hahnemann (1755–1843) investigated alternative procedures. Rather than letting fluids out of the body, Hahnemann pondered, why not impose a balance in the humors by more subtle means? He published his ideas in *The Organon of Homeopathic Medicine* (1810).

Doubtless influenced by the principles of inoculation and vaccination, as developed by the general practitioner

Edward Jenner (1749–1823), Hahnemann focused on the concept of fighting like with like. He suggested that treatment of a medical condition should consist of administering a very dilute dose of substances that, in larger doses, would produce the symptoms that had initially ailed the patient. Interestingly, in Greek, *homeo* translates as "the same," and *pathos* means "suffering." Unfortunately Hahnemann took his idea to an extreme, and began speaking of magical dilutions that, when shaken by the practitioner, would release "immaterial and spiritual power." He believed that with a simple tap of the bottled dilution on the heel of the hand, the practitioner could "double the dilution" of the medicine, that is half the strength yet again, and thus greatly increase its curative power.

Aside from Hahnemann's somewhat illogical notion that the weaker the dose, the more powerful the cure, homeopaths also believed that water possessed a memory of anything it might come into contact with, so a substance diluted to the point of virtual nonexistence would be the most powerful of all. Many modern homeopathists still believe this to be true, but let us hope they have been misled, otherwise our planet's water, which has been subjected to all manner of chemicals and fecal matter over the centuries, would surely be the most toxic substance known to man. Despite the far-out nature of some of Hahnemann's theories, he deserves to be held in fond memory for having saved many a patient from being drained of blood at a time when they needed it most.

As for Hahnemann's principles of dilution: I have conducted my own tests with whiskey and, cross my heart, I can affirm that one drop of single malt in a glass of water will not blow you out of your chair. It is far more effective to drink it neat.

BIBLIOGRAPHY

Berry, Adrian. *Eureka!* London: Harrap Books, 1989.

Boese, Alex. *Elephants on Acid and Other Bizarre Experiments.* London: Pan Books, 2009.

Bynum, William F. *Science and the Practice of Medicine in the Nineteenth Century.* Cambridge: Cambridge University Press, 1994.

———. *The History of Medicine: A Very Short Introduction.* Oxford: Oxford University Press, 2008.

Carroll, Robert Todd. *The Skeptic's Dictionary.* Hoboken, NJ: John Wiley & Sons, 2003.

Friedman, Stanton T., and Kathleen Marden. *Science Was Wrong.* Pompton Plains, NJ: Career Press, 2010.

Goldacre, Ben. *Bad Science.* London: Harper Perennial, 2009.

Lilienfeld, Scott O., Steven Jay Lynn, John Ruscio, and Barry L. Beyerstein. *50 Great Myths of Popular Psychology.* West Sussex, UK: Wiley-Blackwell, 2010.

Plait, Philip C. *Bad Astronomy.* Hoboken, NJ: John Wiley & Sons, 2002.

Pollard, Justin. *Boffinology.* London: John Murray Publishers, 2010.

Porter, Roy. *The Greatest Benefit to Mankind.* New York: HarperCollins, 1997.

Schneider, Reto U. *The Mad Science Book.* London: Quercus, 2008.

Singh, Simon, and Edzard Ernst. *Trick or Treatment.* London: Corgi Books, 2009.

Wanjek, Christopher. *Bad Medicine.* Hoboken, NJ: John Wiley & Sons, 2002.

INDEX

⌘

Note: Page numbers in *italic* refer to illustrations.